THE YEAR OF
THE TAWNY OWL
THE STORY OF
ULE OF DILDAWN

THE YEAR OF
THE TAWNY OWL

THE STORY OF
ULE OF DILDAWN

Paul Thomas

BLANDFORD

First published by Souvenir Press Ltd 1984
This paperback edition first published 1989 by
Blandford Press, an imprint of Cassell,
Artillery House, Artillery Row, London SW1P 1RT

Distributed in Australia by
Capricorn Link (Australia) Pty Ltd,
PO Box 665, Lane Cove, NSW 2066

British Library Cataloguing in Publication Data
Thomas, Paul, *1945-*
    The year of the tawny owl: the story of Ule
    of Dildawn.
    1. Great Britain. Tawny owls. Life cycle
    I. Title
    598′.97

ISBN 0-7137-2100-6

Typeset in Great Britain by
Hazell Watson & Viney Limited
Member of the BPCC Group, Aylesbury, Bucks.
Printed in Great Britain by Cox & Wyman Ltd, Reading, Berks.

❧ CONTENTS ❧

ACKNOWLEDGEMENTS

The production of this book has been a labour of love – not merely on our part, for many people have helped directly by recounting observations and stories, some of which have been incorporated into Ule's own story.

We are particularly grateful to Mrs Jane Daniel of Frome and Mr Loh Chin Fenn, and to Mr Chris Mead of the British Trust for Ornithology and Miss Eunice Overend for checking the accuracy of the story. Like many other skills, observing and interpreting nature is not easy. What we thought we were seeing was not always actually what we saw! Chris and Eunice put us right, although any inaccuracies still remain entirely our responsibility.

Our thanks also go to Mr I. Stewart and Mr J. Wickersham, to Mrs Edith Hoddinott on whose land some of our observations took place and to Miss Gina O'Connor and Mr Stephen Fry for the map of Dildawn.

As far as the text is concerned, Paul is particularly grateful to Mr Michael Bright of the BBC, who over the past few years has encouraged a sympathetic and animal-centred approach to story telling and has always frowned upon the anthropomorphic. We hope we have lived up to his high standards.

We are also very grateful to Tessa Harrow for her encouragement during the project. Her sympathetic appreciation of the countryside aided us in our search for a truthful and balanced description of the Year of the Tawny Owl. Without her editorial direction this book would not have achieved its final, finished form.

Finally, our thanks to our two small daughters, Gaenor and Morwenna, who have tolerated the absence of their parents and, from time to time, accepted second place to a pair of owls, with a degree of equanimity beyond their years.

Paul and Gillian Thomas
Bloomfield

PROLOGUE

I had just finished a very successful radio programme. It had dealt with that remarkable little bird, the Arctic tern, which each year circles the globe, flying from the Arctic to the Antarctic and back. The producer, always full of ideas, suggested that, for our next project, we might work on the tawny owl. I had known very little about Arctic terns before I started; now and again I had seen them on their way to the Farne Islands off the Northumberland coast, and to me they were just terns, seabirds; but in researching the programme I had unravelled an incredible story of endurance and unfailingly accurate navigation. Tawny owls were another matter – I knew a great deal about *them*. They often flew over our tiny Mendip stone cottage, especially in the winter months when they were establishing their territorial rights. Rather an ordinary subject, I thought, an owl; almost like a pigeon or a sparrow. Naturally I kept my doubts to myself when I sat in that BBC office. I cannot afford to turn down work through lack of enthusiasm.

As I drove home through the September sunshine, pushing past the unregulated, snarling traffic of a Bristol rush hour, my mind hop-scotched through my own sightings of tawny owls. Only the Sunday before, when I was out walking on my favourite piece of country, the Mendips, not far from my home, I had seen an old female in the bright light of early evening, sitting bolt upright on a stone wall. Unusual, I thought. She was dozing, but out in the open, exposed. Unfortunately my three year-old daughter decided to rush up to say 'Hello', and off flew the bird into a small ash copse. There she took up a more familiar position, tight against the trunk, hidden, unless you had seen her alight and knew where to look. Then there had been the time last winter – about half past eight in the evening; a murky night; dry, but with low cloud, rain imminent. I was driving along our country lane when a tawny owl swooped out of a field, skimmed low over the hedge and suddenly hesitated directly in front of me. For a moment I thought it was coming at my windscreen. The sudden flash of headlights, I suppose, momentarily disorientated the creature. Then it was off into the black meadows of night, flying sedately on those powerful wings.

I was out of the city now and passing through the villages that stutter along the road leading south to my home. Actually, I thought, I've never been out looking for them. Other birds, yes, but not the tawny. Funny really, because I'd often heard them, up on the Sleight, the hill behind my cottage. Go out to the dustbin after dark and likely as not you will hear a fox, or else the owls.

Over tea with the children I mused about owls. This infuriated my two daughters who soon realized I was not listening to a word they were saying. Thus, in disgrace, on that early autumn evening, I left the cottage at twilight and wandered slowly up the bridle path that runs close behind my house.

*　　*　　*

An untidy gaggle of rooks flopped slowly across the fields, taking their noise into the warm wood behind the village. A storm had been brewing all afternoon and, as the birds settled into the quietness between the trees, it broke, streaking the golden leaves with glinting rain. Thunder rumbled. I pulled up the hood of my storm coat. Distant lightning flashed noisily through leaves and branches. The rooks did not like it. For a few moments they were very restive, then, as darkness came, their squawks faded erratically into silence. It was not complete darkness, not deep blackness, but it was oppressive, heavy with rain above my head. I thought of turning back but did not, because through the creaking, trembling shadows came the melancholy cries of night, long and clear. No merry notes these; haunting, in a reassuring sort of way; cutting through to the quick of my long familiarity and love of these, my known acres. I looked up into the heart of the teeming rain and lipped the dripping wetness. It tasted sweet.

They called again, those apparitions of autumn. Two birds. Male and female, proclaiming their rights to territory through the drumming storm: an area large enough to support themselves and a new family in the coming breeding season. I shivered. Somehow a trickle of water had contrived to sneak down the back of my neck. It is a well known bird song, but filtered through aeons of human consciousness it has become a cry of ghosts. All down the ages owls have worried man, understandably perhaps. Taken generally, birds are lovers of light, but tawny owls most definitely are not. And whereas the nightingale brings joy to man's dark hours, the owl brings dread.

It came again, muffled by a blustering wind. I leaned gently against the trunk of an old oak growing at the edge of the wood, straining my ears. The storm was moving off northwestwards towards Bath. The rain began to slacken, but it was still dark and I had no torch. The fields echoed with a sinister silence – I checked myself. That's funny, I thought. I know this wood; there's nothing to be frightened of.

The birds were silent. Perhaps they were watching me, the erstwhile watcher! In the murky darkness of the woodland I could see little, but with their eyes, one hundred times more efficient than mine in the dark, I would be easy to spot. As if they read my thoughts, the duet began again. The 'hoot' of the male and the 'kewick' of the female. Had they moved? The cries seemed to be coming from a different quarter, or was it the thickening cloud cover playing tricks with my ears? I sighed, then noticed that I had done so and wondered why.

Sad to say, that first evening I turned tail, finding the lure of a log fire at home too strong, to resist. I dripped in through the back door, reached for a towel and began to reappraise my views; but there was no time for thinking. I was back into the bustle of bedtime rituals – reading stories and goodnight kisses. Then, as sleep came to my daughters, I crept downstairs to sit and look deep into the heat of the fire. The black cast-iron fire dogs, firm on their three legs, framed burning logs of apple and oak. Outside, the fingers of the storm had returned to flutter at our small window panes. In the garden wind bustled through the laburnum and lilac. Out there in the darkness was the shady side of night, but inside I was warm and shipshape. The Bristol Cream, tawny in my glass, brought pleasure, and a tiny flicker of excitement twitched into an involuntary smile.

A whole year was to smile with my friendship for them. (They would have none of mine!) Ule, for that's what I christened the male, and Kewick, his mate, took me through the beauty of my own familiar landscape into the unknown: their night, their presence, close to me as my own shadow; a sense of contact, a seeing in the dark. Unmolested (for I did not stare at them), the two birds flourished amid the dappled moonlight. I heard the quiet courtship calls of spring; the aggression shown to other invading owls, the alarmed reactions to an intruding fox; the high-pitched squeaks of bank voles snatched from life by those silent hunters; the chirpings and chippings of emergent new life, and the final silence of death.

This year, their year, has gone forever; yet in a sense it is living still, into the future – not just in the spinning moments of my slowing memory, but in a hundred thousand woods, replicated over a million hectares. For the tawny owl is very common, not just in Europe, but in much of Asia, Arabia and North Africa, too. Although, like all wild

11

creatures, they are shy of man, they are not secretive; we country folk know them well, and even town dwellers hear their cry because many a tawny lives and nests in public parks and large gardens, right in the heart of the biggest city. They flourish in a variety of climates and landscapes, and because they do not mind living close to us, it is not difficult for anyone to find them.

So Ule's wood is not a secret place, although I shall not describe its geography in detail, nor its location – it is hidden in my mind. Indeed its outline, its slopes, the stream, the hidden meadow and the waterfall could be part of any wood. Private. Full of unseen life. And although there is nothing really dramatic in this short story, it is adventure all the same, for these common tales of ordinary life are made mysterious by the night, told in the dark, without sight and often with just the slightest wisp of sound.

*   *   *

The tawny owl, often called the brown owl, is the most widespread owl in Europe and the Middle East. It is a moderately large, mottled bird with a big head and a round face. It is about fifteen inches long; the female slightly larger than the male.

On top it is a rufous brown colour, streaked. There are conspicuous whitish patches on its shoulders and wings. The underparts are buff, broadly streaked and barred dark brown. Two colour phases occur, one less rufous and more grey.

1

SEPTEMBER STORM

Rain was teeming down, masking sight, sound and scent. Ule sat in silence on a dripping branch. He was easy to recognize, a biggish bird with a very striking face; two huge saucer-like depressions covered the front of his head. Kewick, slightly larger as all female tawny owls tend to be, perched close by. They sat, male and female, at the centre of their territory, an area of woodland they had conquered and defended fiercely against other intruding owls. For more than two years they had been together and their routines were well established. Tawny owls mate for life – a partnership important and instinctive, geared to survival. So the two birds knew each other well, knew each other's hunting tactics, each other's preferred perch and, most important, each other's voice calling in the dark.

The storm blew on. Curtains of water filled the valley, covering the dark, steep slopes with a slowly moving heaviness. No birds like a lot of rain, least of all owls; the line between waterlogging and waterproofing is very fine. So Ule perched close to the damp trunk and was perfectly still.

In sudden sharp blasts, the whole wood was lit as brightly as noonday, but it was not the gold of the sudden sun; this light was harsh and silver. There was another flash, perfectly reflected in the dark brown lenses of Ule's hunting eyes, but neither owl moved. The fierceness of the storm was overhead; it penetrated all the dark ways and, for one deafening second, thunder and lightning were one. Where the greatest light fell,

high over St Stephen's Falls, there was a sizzling crack. Above the cliffs that bounded Dildawn's stream, a tall tree fell. There was a tearing, groaning roar: the earth's skin had been cut and badly grazed. The splash pool below the waterfall became choked with sandstone loam and dying leaves, and the stream itself, already gorged with floodwater, struggled to free itself of tangled branches, fallen roots and solid limbs. Everywhere was in turmoil.

Ule had seen it all before, autumn's rain. Indeed both birds had seen off a good few storms, some worse than this, and the seasons too – five times they had watched the annual march of life and death, there, in that wood; a procession no human had witnessed, for the owls had a night time vision when flowers were closed and shadows were open sounds.

The wind bustled untidily. It was an uninspiring spectacle: the wood full of crackling air and dripping rustles; birds hiding, shunning the drips; rabbits in their burrows, hedgehogs and badgers wide awake but tight in their nests; woodmice, legs splayed flat against the soft floor of their holes, panting slowly and quietly. The wind raved on. Even the great oaks flailed their arms and early dead leaves whirled upwards into the writhing darkness; and Ule and Kewick sat waiting, through all the noise they listened.

On most nights the wood was a quiet place. At its edge a road skirted the contours – Friggle Street, as the local humans called it. Cold and dark they found it, so Friggle it had become, centuries before, and Friggle it remained even when horse and cart were replaced by cars and flashing headlights. It was not a busy road, few humans travelled it, but nonetheless Ule was wary of it, and he had good reason. Close to his right eye ran a very slight scar, an indistinct disturbance amidst the feathers. Not long after he was out of the egg, when he was still learning to hunt, he had come close to Friggle Street and glided down to look. It was a dark night, but a powerful light with a sharp whip had caused him fright and pain. The fright he still remembered, a dull, aching memory. So Ule never came to the road at the side of his wood. Unknown to him, fate had smiled on him that dark night, for car aerials maim many an owl.

But it was not memory which caused most disturbance, it was the noise the road carried which invaded the daily living pattern of Dildawn. Occasionally, during the daytime, a very loud motorbike or an overloaded lorry started shock waves through the gnarled trunks, sending up a swirling mass of autumn finches, or agitating spring rooks nesting near the bridle path. At night the disturbances were different.

The engine noise was still there, but more – beams of light shot straight across the curving tarmac, snapping the owls' fleeting presence even in the deepest parts of the shadowy wood. However, in those small hours full of storm, the road was empty, and so was the wood; the scurrying, scuttling night waited for the storm to blow itself out.

Moonrise came, and the storm faded westwards across distant fields. Between the breaking clouds, the moon's first quarter appeared, momentarily, without lustre. The rain had passed but drops still fell within the wood. Ule's dark eyes picked out one such drop of interrupted rain, which fell noisily from dying leaf to dying leaf. And while he stared deeply into the shadows of the night, his ears were sharp. Through the trembling stillness he heard the roar of the waterfall. St Stephen's Falls were constant in his mind, always filling the wood with noise, either controlled and muted mutterings of warm summer or, as on that autumn night, a fierce roar. So he listened carefully, discounting the unneeded sounds. Although his ear holes were hidden by feathers they were as large as a cat's, and as eager. They strained to pick up the tiniest sound of pricking claws on wet leaves. He knew that, with the dying of the storm, Dildawn would soon become a busy place, full of small mammals out to rummage through the remains of the night.

As he waited through the long minutes, a boar badger intervened by ambling out of his sett, high up on the slope. It wasn't long before his black and white shadow was moving along his well-worn track with typical carelessness, stepping noisily on twigs brought down by the evening's storm. Kewick had heard him long before the first twig had snapped. She had quite easily identified the padding rustles, but Ule turned his head to look. There was no room in his eye sockets to move his eyes more than a fraction so, in typical owl fashion, he rotated his head. Brock lumbered onwards into the depths of the wood to hunt his staple diet: slugs and worms (in all that dampness there were plenty wriggling and sliding across the woodland floor).

The quietness grew and the darkness lightened. Ule returned to his patient watching, waiting, but Kewick moved slightly and there was the scratch of talons on the oak's bark. Ule remained perfectly still as he saw his mate launch out on the shaken light of the quiet moon. Silently she went, for a fine velvety fringe around the edge of her flight feathers muffled all her movements. Her indistinct shadow fell across ruined walls, built years ago when the scar of the quarry face was buff and fresh, and men with time to subdivide this scrubby portion of the earth thought such territorial rights important. She glided down, over the still, deep pool below the waterfall and, where the water gleamed smoothly into paws and shining claws of moonshine, she dropped her talons; below her the stuttering stones had taken confidence and built a small island: Alder Island. She alighted on an ancient, water-loving tree, nestled close to its trunk and merged with the still shadows, settling to wait and watch again.

Any meticulous observer would have seen what she had spotted: trickles of watery earth flowing down the bank to the swift stream. Like all tawny owls, Kewick had remarkably keen night sight. Her eyeballs were huge and tubular, so large that the most efficient lens possible could be fitted into a limited space; that lens collected and concentrated the feeble light of night. She could in fact see in light intensities one hundredth of the minimum required by man – could almost see in the dark. The earth trickle continued. After the storm a vole was carrying out alterations to its tunnel system. Patience was the game, and the owl remained motionless.

The sky cleared of cloud. Stars pricked. The moonshine was vague but there was light enough. On her alder branch Kewick wiped her eyes alert. Equipped with three pairs of eyelids, she used the third, transparent membrane so that her keen watching was not interrupted. The earth trickle had almost stopped when she heard a movement at the mouth of the hole. She froze, although inside her breast beat a violent heart, five times as fast as any human's, and quietly, so quietly that nothing, save perhaps an adjacent owl, could hear, she stood up and braced her feet. Each foot had three toes facing forward and one backwards, but the outer toe was reversible, it could face both ways. No tawny owl is happy perching for long periods. Kewick's natural standing position was flat footed, resting on her thick, padded soles, with claws drawn up into downy feathers. Humans might call her talons feet, but she used them much more dexterously. Really they were a pair of hands to her, as well as supports for standing still. The undersides of those 'hand-feet' were a dull pinkish colour, tipped with eight long, dark brown hooked claws, razor sharp, four to each foot. The main grip came from the inner and back toes, almost like a first finger and thumb. The other two claws were for support and balance. Cruel those claws were, with the vice-like potential of death, and yet, so delicate and precise was Kewick's use of them that she could land in complete gentleness and silence, with those very claws withdrawn into her feathers. But at that moment she was wakeful, alert, and her claws were sharp, merciless and ready.

A blunt nose appeared at the bankside entrance; whiskers trembled, tasted the air, felt for rising scents. The bank above that part of the stream was a steep wall of wet mud, about two feet high. Kewick stared at it. There was a sudden plop. If that had been her intended victim it had escaped into the grey ripples of the stream. But Kewick did not move, even when an eerie, wheezy bark broke into the quietness of the clearing air and surprised her. She heard, she interpreted and was steely silent. A dog fox was also up and about his night time search for food. More long moments passed by. The fox moved on, leaving Kewick high on her silent perch.

By now there was a slight chill in the air, but although the temperature fell the owl still stood motionless. A late moth, made sluggish by the cold, whirred close to her perch. Still Kewick waited and finally patience brought its own reward. From under the dying ferns on the flaggy side of the stream there came a rustle; above the steep muddy bank there was a slight movement. It was not a rodent: instead an old frog, hunting worms brought to the surface by the rain, was quietly crawling about. A fat frog. A careless frog. An acceptable frog! On her silent wings she flew back to her mate who was waiting quietly at the centre of their woodland empire (her talons were so powerful that her victim had not even survived their first strike of the night). She alighted at her perch, and there was a moment's hesitation in her hunting ritual. She bit the creature's head, as she always did, to crush the skull, and she noted her mistake: the frog was a toad! So Kewick considered, for toads contain a toxin which even owls find distasteful, but despite her disappointment she swallowed the creature, whole.

*   *   *

Orion's belt now twinkled boldly, high on the southern horizon, and lower, more distant Sirius, the dog star – part of the late-night sky map for that day of the year. The stars in the sky changed, but with a slow regularity, and the structure of the wood changed too, but only in superficial detail. Trees fell, lay, rotted and disappeared, other trees sprouted, grew and towered, all in such slow motion that Ule's life span saw little of a tree's cycle from seedling to toppling woodland geriatric. But what he saw he knew: the untidy slopes full of fallen limbs, broken branches and tumbled stones; the oaks, not as litter across a lighted landscape, but as shadowed cover for prey, places against which to watch and wait.

It was in that familiarity that Ule now stood still and was confident of a catch. A decaying tree stump, remnant of a harvested oak, was the

focus of his attention. Three holes had been tunnelled into its rotting roots. In the darkness there was a movement, but not on the litter around the stump, instead, on a living trunk, four yards distant. There two grey shadows, hermaphrodites, had rasped their way through fungi and algae; they paused, and another instinct triggered off different behaviour. The great grey slug, seven and a half inches long, had identified a mate in the perfect dampness of that night. With wavering tentacles and weaving heads they circled each other, came closer and closer, licking each other, eating their slime. An owl might take them, but more likely the rapacious and ever hungry shrew. That was their risk.

At the stream's side a hungry water vole munched greedily, but Kewick was not there to see. She perched close to her mate, peering across the south facing slope. She heard the water bubbling against the bigger stones, but more important, at a short glide's distance there was another, quieter sound. Ule heard it too. The small mammals of the wood were venturing out into the night. Wings spanning a full yard glided silently, great with eyes and keen ears, and two strong-taloned feet were spread wide for a sharp, firm clasp. There was one moment's consideration while he calculated prey size and suitability, and then the strike. He returned to his perch to bite the skull and swallow the woodmouse whole.

On the damp floor a snail's horned head moved steadily through the dripping air, and almost as quickly the woodland floor rustled and bloomed. The moisture had brought out the fungi, and fast fruiting bodies broke through the litter of early autumn, sinister yet familiar. Some were edible and attractive, others deadly and vile smelling: panther cap and fly agaric, chanterelle and jew's ear, beaf steak and honey, names as imaginative and profuse as the fungi themselves.

Distant from the owls' oak there was more movement, vigorous and desperate. A worm wriggled, struggled to extricate itself from the sure grasp of a shrew. Dildawn was heaving, writhing, fighting its way towards morning light. A small reservoir of rain, held tight by a gently cupped leaf, suddenly broke its delicate dam, fell and exploded noisily on a stem just above the water vole's head. Instinctively and with precision, the small creature jumped into one of the back entrances to its watery hideaway, and as it hid there was more rustling, a great shuffling, and a heavy creature loomed nearer and larger; not a deer, for they tripped lightly, but a noisy sniffing and snuffling around rotting and decaying tree stumps. The boar badger was searching out a delicacy he had first discovered as a young cub: fungi. Hardly disguising his delight, he selected carefully, snaffled and champed away with relish. Distant from him, but still in Dildawn, hard against the quarry face, there was more movement. In flagstone crevices, hidden behind thick wrappings of ivy, another form of life bustled and shuffled against the coarse sandstone; ultrasonic squeaks tested the echoing air. The pipistrelle, commonest of British bats, was moving about. All day and half the night it had hung upside down in that dark place; now its four-chambered heart pumped warming blood round the tiny two-inch long body and across the eight inches of membrane that formed the wings.

Autumn was their time for love. Male and female bat. Together they shuffled out into the night time air, but they flew singly, the darkling sky bright with noise that, scattered across the dying wind, told the hunting bat where night-flying insects and moths took their paths. Scents and sounds brushed around the alert head and powerful breast. She lived off that lightless air, the female bat. Each night, during the months of warmth, she hawked up and down, flitting with agility and accuracy along a well-defined path, always at the woodland's edge. Ule and Kewick did not hear her that night, for they were preoccupied with each other. Close and quietly they called, murmuring tentative phrases of song to each other. Soon, in a matter of days, would come the powerful proclamation of their right to own Dildawn, but as yet the owls were alone and gentle with each other.

Apart from Ule and Kewick, most activity in Dildawn took place at its borders. Cattle and sheep coughed and shivered at the meadow's edge. Badgers and foxes fed out into the surrounding areas, even shy rabbits hopped outwards into the grass. Only timid, tiny mammals and their predators filled the branching deeps of Dildawn's heartland. For the second time that night, Kewick left her daytime roost, glided quietly down to Alder Island and there returned to her watchfulness. Ule sat and noted her disappearing form, counted the moments, then called, and across the quiet slopes came the expected reply. Kewick had heard him, heard him well and replied. Dildawn was theirs. There were no intruders, only a young buck rabbit, pausing nervously at the clear sounds.

The bat hawked on. She found Dildawn suited her well: there was water to drink and nurture an assortment of insects, there was her favourite tree, the common sallow, and the quarry face with its ivy to hide ideal niches for long restful days of dark, damp coolness. Squeak. Echo. Squeak. Echo. Squeak. Echo. Thirty times a second she called and listened in that impeccable sequence of broadcasting and receiving. Unlike the owls, patience was not in her repertoire for, like her cousin the shrew, when awake her life was frenetic. Already her gaping mouth had captured twenty-five midges and a late-flying clothes moth, newly emerged from its larval state in one of Ule's disgorged pellets. In that darkness, while Ule waited silently, she battled with a giant, a dor beetle close on half her size. Immediately, without interrupting her flight, she arched her body forward and swung up her tail, trying to contain the creature within the membranous pocket: but the insect was not so easily dispatched and she flitted off her flight path to her night time perch – twisted sallow overhanging the ride. At the foot of the tree a careful observer would have found discarded cases, tough legs and inedible moth wings, because several times each night the pipistrelle travelled there to feast on larger prey, too big for consumption on the wing.

Slowly the wood filled with the slight scent of drying grass. A taste of moonlight glinted on dark hollies. Ule watched on. Suddenly the scratching of claws on bark, a swish of crisp autumnal leaves: morning was coming. Up and early a grey squirrel moved along a branch, too close for Ule's comfort. Through the intermittent clatter of acorns from the canopy came a sharp and severe response, a decisive call announcing the owl's presence. The young squirrel did not wait to argue. In panic, directly, almost clumsily, he jumped through the tree tops, and Ule ignored the movement, with his eyes. Still with the red tints of summer on his haunches, the grey squirrel leaped from bough to bough, shaking the leaves noisily. Haste took the creature to the end of an overhanging bough; he jumped, stretched out in faith for another branch. Desperately he clutched at the leaves; in his fear he had misjudged. All four feet outspread, he fell to the litter and bramble below and there was an audible thump. Only then did Ule look, but the fall was screened by dying bracken. There was a great deal of scratching and scrabbling, a scrambling through the undergrowth, and into the safety of the hidden distance went the squirrel, shaken, but unharmed.

Dimpsey, the between light, filled the valley, crept up the wooded slopes and penetrated deep into a thick-grown thorn where a puffed-out blackbird was roosting; it nudged him into wakefulness and, as he shuffled, Kewick called. It had been a long night, made short for hunting by the storm, and although the light was coming fast the owls still searched for prey.

The pipistrelle suddenly flitted up the slope, back to the quarry face. There she pitched her head upwards, clung with thumb and toe, shuffled round, and scuttled head downwards into her daytime crevice to groom herself. Slowly her breathing rate faltered, her spleen filled up with blood and, while her heart slowed down, her body temperature fell.

A blackbird scolded an owl shadow. An aggressive robin, eager to lay claim to a winter kingdom, started up early and the old boar badger heard him: after walking his estate he had ambled back to his high sett and shuffled low, below ground. This was shared time, those stuttering moments of half light when the hunters of day might glimpse their night time colleagues. Buzzard and sparrowhawk were up and ready to kill, shrews, as always, were eating furiously and Ule and Kewick still flew the open pathways – but not to hunt – to hide, for the male led his mate through the widening shapes of morning to a hidden perch, tight against a densely dark and sheltered trunk. From his chosen site they prepared to rest and listen the day away.

2

OCTOBER DAY

A month had gone by in the steady march of the falling year. One day, shortly after dawn, when Ule and Kewick had just retreated into their daytime perch, woodpigeons exploded into the early morning air with violent wing beats. Small birds followed them up and away out of the woodland. The owls sensed that a daytime hunter had come close. Yet although there was a great clattering of fear about their ears they did not look for safety in flight. Instead they stood still, their feathers frozen, and lengthened their shape into mottled camouflage.

It was a man dressed in a brilliant, fluorescent orange anorak. He paused at the stile and raised his binoculars to a flock of finches flying noisily away to one side of the bridle path. His foot thudded firmly down, two inches away from the round hole of the woodmouse. Hidden safe from the day, the small creature quivered silently, small crumbs of rich soil falling onto its sleek fur. Above, at the earth's surface, a blackbird shot out of a hawthorn bush at ankle height and rushed off. Unperturbed the man walked on, fleeing birds disappearing before him. Unconscious of his own noise and smell, he tramped on, delighted to see a white-tailed rabbit bundling itself into a burrow below some tangled brambles. Those creatures which did not flee waited, huddled, and listened for the footsteps to pass by and fade into the distance. Up the slope he climbed, breathing heavily with the effort. The owls watched and noted, but they were safe and they relaxed into a momentary doze.

'Scaaaaaarg!' Suddenly and again, 'Scaaaaaaaarg!' The owls looked. A jay! Pink and blue, a touch of black and white come to a nearby oak – a huge broken-headed hulk. Bright sunlight broke through the fading canopy and the noisy bird was clear for all to see. Tense, but firm in his hidden day, Ule watched the jay's pillage. It flew in, landed, leaned over, grabbed an acorn from its cup and swallowed it. And another. Again it pouched the oak seed, then took a third, but this time it held the acorn in its beak and flew off, away from the wooded slopes, down into the hidden meadow. Its most favoured hiding place for acorns was under a thin covering of leaves and twigs at the wood's edge.

Another large bird flew into the morning wood, a rook. It landed at the side of a large puddle which all but covered the width of the bridle path and leaned forward to take a beakful of water; by arching its neck it let the water run down its throat, but there was no time for a second beakful. Again the pigeons exploded noisily into the treetops. Finches flew away. A fluorescent jacket bobbed conspicuously over the wet grassed fields – the bird watcher was returning to his car after 'sampling the dawn chorus'. Within a few moments he reached his vehicle, took off his anorak and threw it on to the back seat, then he looked about him, breathed in deeply, gave a sigh of satisfaction, got in and drove off, much to the startled disgust of a young rabbit browsing close to the roadside.

Like most of the creatures in Dildawn, Ule and Kewick were afraid of the sight and sound of man. They disliked the heavy careless noise, the strange scents and the unpredictable habits. Yet few days were without human interference, for Dildawn was managed as a commercial venture and Longland, the meadow at the heart of the woodland, was used by a local farmer for his stock. Then there was Greyfield, an isolated house close to Friggle Street, on the northern edge of the woodland. The married couple who lived there walked the woodland rides regularly, especially the woman. She was well known to Ule as she crept quietly about, in her dark greens. Although he was wary of her, because she was quiet and careful and because she too lived in the wood, Ule and Kewick were as used to her presence as they were to the badgers up the slope. Much more disturbing were the day trippers and picnickers for, although the waterfall was not advertised as a tourist attraction, local people, especially those from the nearby villages of Ston Gurney and Hallow's Trow, knew it well. Children especially, in the summer, raced along the stream, climbed the rocks and ledges of the falls and made much noise.

No creatures knew Dildawn better than Ule and Kewick. Some

humans thought they knew it well, for they had named it and recorded the name: Dildawn. Like so many country names no one could remember why or how those wooded slopes had acquired their name. Longland was easy to interpret: the flat valley bottom between the two arms of woodland was a long finger of pasture, less than a hundred yards wide but more than three quarters of a mile long. But Dildawn, what of that name? For a wood of the night it seemed apt, but as few men ever saw it under its cloak of darkness there must have been more to the name than that.

Man had a name for every acre of Ule's territory and Kewick's haunts. The waterfall was named after a local saint, Stephen, whose chapel lay close to the stone-parapeted Bendal's Bridge; Greyfield had been christened a century and a half before when nearby coal mines disgorged grey slag, and although in the time of Ule and Kewick the tip was flat topped and overgrown, it was still there. Greyfield was a paddock, close by the grandiosely titled Greyfield Lodge. There were other names, not mentioned on the map, but hidden in the minds of those humans who loved the wood: the jolly imaginings of children and the more long lasting and romantic descriptions – 'wintersett' and 'owl tree' – used by the woman who lived at Greyfield.

Ule knew nothing of names. Visitors he saw, during the day, or more often heard, for he always tried to let the creatures of the day pass him by as he hid behind thick ivy or in dense hawthorn. That was not always possible, especially in late autumn and winter when the wood became a busy place. The great flood of migration brought fieldfares from Latvia, redwings from Norway, blackbirds from Sweden, song thrushes from Germany, and from all the fields and pastures, nests and roosts, the tiny birds of England – wren, goldcrest and dunnock, pecking about in the undergrowth, and the titmice concentrated in their large roving parties, often one hundred in a group, splitting open shells, feeding hungrily on ash keys and calling constantly to each other. Although the owls were set back, with their talons resting on a dark roost, Ule and Kewick heard them all.

Some sounds they ignored, like the greedy gobblings of the fieldfares in the old yew tree, up near Greyfield, but their ears were keen to the calls of the diurnal birds of prey – the Cloud Hill buzzards which watched the spinning day, hanging high and patient, eyes piercing each moment of life in Longland and Dildawn; and the sparrowhawks amidst the larch, a streak of blue grey, a blaze of yellow eyes – they were the real danger, with their pell mell dash, twisting and turning, seeking out the unsuspecting and greedy. Neither male nor female hawk hunted

mice. Theirs was a quick flurry on a tide of terror, followed by frantic alarm calls down the woodland ride and a cream feather drifting across the cold air where moments before a gobbling fieldfare had fed hungrily in the yew.

It was through the branches of their daytime perch that the owl pair heard other sounds of dangerous irritation: a real threat – the soft approaching sounds of a foraging flock of small birds. As the flock made its slow, meandering way through the woodland there was the continuous sound of contact calls helping the group to keep its loose-knit cohesion. The birds followed a looping track crossing previous daytime pathways, coming close to the owls then moving away, but each time their pathway approached the oak tree Ule stiffened. Although the tiny birds were in a flock, each fed singly in its own private space; now and again, when one small bird violated the preserve of another, there was an outburst of scolding and the beating of furious wings, a peck was followed by a retreating flurry. Mock battles punctuated the business of feeding, but always after each attempted invasion, the successful defender reverted immediately to its search for food, as did the invader.

All winter the birds fed like that, for in each other's company there was more time to feed and less need to look for danger – one hundred pairs of eyes were better than one! Yet it took but one to see, and one did: a great tit, probing the ivy of the old oak, saw the familiar shape of the owls, interpreted it as danger, kept its distance but showed alarm with tail and wing. The bird screamed out a wide, raucous repetition. In all directions went the call and from all directions came small birds looking for the conspicuous pointers of wing flapping and tail cocking which indicated danger. Neither owl tried to escape; tight and still they remained, firm against the trunk, waiting for the mobbing birds to tire and lose interest, as they always did.

Chance had made that old oak a bad roosting place: thanks to a great tit the whole of Dildawn knew where to find a pair of tawny owls on that autumn day and every creature had been warned to avoid the spot. Ironically the fuss and display had the same effect on Ule and Kewick; neither would choose that tree again, but for those moments of tumult they sat defiant. Kewick flashing her light-adapted eyes, harsh against the filtered sun.

*   *   *

Days bustled with pigeon and jay, cock pheasants boasted and, despite the cold, a few flowers struggled to bloom: late bramble and, low down in the hedge sheltered from wind and rain, even a scattering of red campion and the blue specks of scabious; open ivy flowers attracted a few lingering hoverflies, but in general the hedge was turning brown. A fierce October had bequeathed sure signs of winter; bracken weathered first, but remained upright in dense, dead stands, then hazel and field maple, and finally the gold and saffron of the whole deciduous wood blazed red. But the glory of autumn always faded at the dying of each day; the sun took with it colour and brightness, leaving only the silhouettes of night and its own reflection, huge and rose red, rising high over the dark trees: the Hunter's Moon.

In the moonshine close to Longland's edge an old hare began to stir. Since morning he had lain up in the wood, not in dense cover like his cousin the rabbit, but on an open, draughty place, reassured by his clear view of the land around him, knowing that if he could see, he could escape. All day he had rested on a boat-shaped, trodden parcel of land, his fur matching the patchy colour of the woodland edge. He had come to Dildawn to digest the gleanings of the previous night; a curious sight: licking at his anus, taking up large, soft undigested pellets of food – not the hard droppings of waste, but nourishment for survival. All day he had chewed them thoroughly, but by dusk the store was exhausted and he had to gather again. So he stood up and with great care went loping through the dusk, rattling tall, dead stalks of wild hemlock, pausing as he heard a noisy flock of starlings drown the soft inward pipings of a bullfinch and, infiltrating the chatter of the starlings, another sound – owls stirring. Ule was stretching his wings and giving the first call of his night. It was nine minutes past sunset and another of man's days had ended, but for Ule, as for many other creatures in Dildawn, the round of daily activity was just beginning. A woodmouse, wide eyed but crouched and anxious, listened and twitched its whiskers nervously. Without great care, the fate of that small mammal's night could be to feed the strength of a master of the night air: Ule.

3

NOVEMBER

The sound of wings was everywhere, seeming much louder in the mist, as if the damp, thick air impeded their movement and drove the birds to greater effort. A rush of starlings, eager to leave the trees for the open fields, passed Ule and Kewick, but the owls clung close to their hiding place in a hawthorn. As the starlings drifted away Ule moved slightly on his branch; the year was becoming chill and dismal, yet, despite the closeness of the penetrating weather, he could hear in the gloom the 'chak-chak-chak-chak' of morning activity and the confidential 'chup-chup-chup-chup' replies as fieldfare and redwing fed happily on ice-coated berries. Fog was not an unknown occurrence in Dildawn, but it still seemed to dull Ule's sharp senses.

The night had been starry and clear and full of successful hunting, but with the sun and morning had come the bewildering wet and clinging world, and it had thickened into fog, shrouding everything. After the initial movements and songs of the rising day, the woodland had fallen into an eerie quietness: a formless landscape of utter solitude. Distantly came the muffled call of a crow, then silence returned.

Suddenly a shattering crash burst upon the intense quiet; a startled bird, shapeless in the fog, hurtled into a bush. A blackbird panicked suddenly and shrieked murder down between the white trunks. A stamping and a snorting sank deep into the woodland, mercilessly breaking the crust of soft moss, crushing and trampling deep the sprouting leaves of next year's bluebells, smashing their wet sheathed

bulbs. Cattle had got into Dildawn: lively young bullocks, curious and confused. A gate had been left unfastened and one inquisitive creature had pushed it open and led the whole herd into the wood.

A woodmouse scuttled for safety as an earthquake wrecked its home, its intricate system of tunnels, front and back doors destroyed by the heavy-sinking hooves. The sounds of the bullocks were familiar, but they were peculiarly close. Ule heard them and stirred into complete motionlessness. The fog was thinning but it still impeded vision. Kewick, not far from her mate, lengthened into her defensive posture. The cattle bumbled along the bridle path at the foot of the slope, bumping awkwardly into each other; one, more adventurous than the rest, half jumped, half staggered up the steep incline and bulbs, small stones, leaf litter and soil rolled down in a miniature avalanche. A snail shell was crushed into oozing wetness. There was more scuffling and a sudden ray of sun picked out the red and green moss on the floor of a small clearing, as several young cattle blundered into the eerie light and stood still, bemused. Behind them their deep footprints were filling up with cloud-clay water.

The cattle made both owls uneasy. Ule scratched at the bark and flapped noiselessly out into the lightness of the wood, and Kewick followed him. The mist was lifting and their square shapes were clearly to be seen as they changed their daytime roost. Ule was ahead by several yards and Kewick heard him let out a strange, strangulated hoot; a swarm of tiny birds, made bold by their numbers, had chosen to mob the owl and Kewick, too, as she flew on. It was an inconvenience and an irritation, but the predators of night retreated into the dense coverts of daytime, away from the finches, away from the cattle, to a place where marauders would not find them.

It was just one sad day in the weeks of the decline and fall of the year; there was little brightness in the sky and Ule and Kewick were not disturbed again as they sat out the light, waiting for it to dim by a factor of one million. When they rested they kept three claws forward, but with night the outer flexible toe would swing round towards the back in readiness, for when they struck the owls always had two claws forward and two back.

They stirred. Kewick preened herself and Ule shook open his wings. Four big brown, unblinking eyes were at once alert to any movement on the leaf litter below. Clouds scudded across the face of the moon, flecking the night with long, deep darkness, but neither owl was entirely dependent upon sight; at night time light is often unreliable, and the owls made use of their other keenest sense: their uncanny hearing.

Both of them could locate the wispiest sound, neither had to wait for their prey to squeak; a sophisticated filtering system enabled them to process all sound signals and locate them both horizontally and vertically.

Ule's ears, like those of his mate, were set lopsided on the skull. The right ear was directed slightly upward and was more sensitive to sounds coming from above, whereas the left ear was pointed downwards and responded to sounds from below. The whole of the owl's face was so shaped that it focused all sounds to the ears; the tightly packed feathers of the two face-saucers acted like the external pinnae of human ears and, just like a man cupping his hand to his ear, so both owls could move their plumage and change the shape of their ear aperture. It was not a dark world in which Ule lived and thrived. He sat with his mate in a bright, if sunless earth, full of sounds which sparkled through his senses and, from all the noises, he created a sound picture of the wood. It was not Dildawn by radar, for that was the bat's map, but it was Dildawn by acute and accurate observation and location in the dark.

Still the owls sat and listened to and through the rustling darkness, hearing all the tell-tale bustlings. Higher up on the slope the badger had hesitated at the entrance of her sett. The sow, mate of the old boar, wavered cautiously and tested the air for scents before ambling out and waddling over to a nearby tree. There she stretched her claws and reached up to scrape them against the old trunk. It was unusual for her to be out and about before the boar, but for once she was and, like him, she was noisy. For several long moments there was the clear, irritating sound of rasping across the oak's inch-thick bark. Then she moved across to the crisp, dead bracken, gathering it in bundles. The day had been dry and sun-filled, the bracken had dried well and now the sow profited from it; she replaced the old, soiled bedding of her nest with clean, sweet-smelling, fresh but dead vegetation. And while she was busy changing her bed linen, in the field the dog fox was on the prowl.

Ule heard them both. In Longland the grass was thin; in that dying time of the year the field voles had been forced to live in smaller and smaller areas, for their lightly covered runs had become increasingly insecure. The fox sniffed through the dark, rusty moonlight on a russet coat. Silently he slipped over brambles and low branches like a cat, his tail flowing behind him and his body undulating in perfect balance. The low, red moon was big above the horizon and the dog fox was a careful shadow. He pounced with precision, snapping as he fell on his prey. Again he stalked and again he pounced and again he was successful. Hunting was excellent so, as he often did on such nights, he scrabbled a larder for himself and buried a cache of nourishing food (like many of the other mammals of the wood), a store against the hungry nights when hunting would not be so good and prey less plentiful. Clouds covered the moon again, leaving the fox to work in deep darkness, and he was quiet.

The owl pair heard all these noises clearly, but there were other sounds, slighter, but for them much more important: mice. Mice squabbling, squeaking away in audible and ultrasonic frequencies. Ule picked up their rustles and squeaks. He turned his head, waited for one more sound to confirm position, then glided confidently through the night air on muffled flight feathers, his head pointing at the sound source. Too late the vole felt the swish of air as Ule flung forward his talons and in complete blackness reached out to snatch the prey. In one short heartbeat, Ule followed the zigzag path of frustrated escape, talons aligned with the body axis of the victim, and he returned to his perch with the catch. Kewick paid little heed to him and his return; she had concentrated on other sounds. A woodmouse had climbed through a hawthorn bush, about three feet up. It had clambered about with a great deal of agility and, as far as Kewick was concerned, with a great deal of noise. The small creature was making for some rosehips growing into the thorn, and, surrounded by the bush, it was quite safe. Kewick could do no more than note its position and listen.

Night was beginning to fill out with a variety of sounds and noises. The female badger had finished cleaning out her sett and had begun to groom herself, scratching her fur loudly and energetically. In a distant hedge bottom there was a scuffling as a hedgehog searched out plump insects which had spent the warm summer days fattening themselves, growing and multiplying; fat insects make for fat hedgehogs and fat hedgehogs survive winter hibernation. The little black snout glistened and snuffled along the length of the shallow ditch. Already the animal's sleeping time outmeasured his waking hours, but he was still eating and it would be another month before he slipped finally into his long sleep of winter. All the inhabitants of the night time wood bustled and prepared for the trials of the coming winter. There was another woodmouse in another bush, again about three feet up. Kewick heard it. It had scurried there and had made a very useful find. In a long-abandoned blackbird's nest was a cache of fallen berries. Accident and gravity had brought the berries, timidity and fear of the night had driven the mouse, and there they met. Another noisy feast safe from the owls' talons.

The clouds cleared, light flashed bright. Kewick flew off and away across the wood to Alder Island, but Ule reverted to his patient watching. Although his world was not one of illuminated shapes and colours, he blinked open his eyes. The top lid fell momentarily, then he concentrated, tightly sifting the night, his downward deflected beak leaving clear his field of vision for his forward facing eyes to scan the bright shadows. The moon was high and Ule gazed intently, bobbing and pivoting on the branch in order to get several viewpoints of the same piece of woodland floor. Although his field of vision was narrow, for three quarters of that view it was binocular and very accurate. The hedgehog had waddled into view; Ule watched him hurry across the leaf litter and saw the spiny creature bustle into the undergrowth. Overhead the slight wind scattered the clouds, then aided their regrouping. The moon was hidden again and Ule resumed his listening, but the waiting continued.

Night deepened and sounds became more urgent. A shrew twitched its long nose urgently, keeping close to its long-favoured run; it was a creature of habit, and was too busy eating to have time to explore. Ule heard the sound of its claws, but did not recognise it for what it was, a foul smelling, evil tasting prey. Instead he increased his interest, the plumage at the edge of his face twitched into alertness. Shrews are short lived; few if any survive more than one winter and the shrew that Ule heard was an old man – a year old; it was trying to extend its autumn territory into winter, for as prey became less easy to find it needed a bigger and bigger area to satisfy its insatiable appetite. So, not unexpectedly in that evening hour, two probing noses came nostril to nostril. The other shrew was young, of the summer's brood. There was the shrill chatter of deadly threats. The odds were stacked against the old shrew, for the fight between the two tiny creatures would be to the death; but fate intervened. Ule snatched his prey, disturbed a few fallen oak leaves and missed by a nose whisker the puzzled veteran. The short-sighted shrew sniffed and scuttled onwards: after such an output of energy he needed food, there was no other consideration. With strong, slow flaps of his powerful wings, Ule returned to his perch and bit hard at the tiny creature's skull, noting that it was shrew. However, like all tawny owls, Ule lacked much sense of smell and did not seem to notice the offensive taste as he dealt with his prey in the usual way and swallowed it whole.

The moon sank down into the black of night to join Aquarius and Pegasus which had long since fallen below the western horizon, yet there was still light: Cassiopeia high above and the dog stars down in the southern sky. Clear and chill, the night reached down to touch the

narrow ride at Greyfield's edge; there another restless creature, the bank vole, concentrated with deliberation, chewing on the tender bark of a newly established oak, planted last autumn by a forgetful squirrel. In the flecked depths of Dildawn's darkness the small creature seemed unconcerned by the badger's smacking lips. The owls were distant and the badger had visited to feast on Greyfield's yew berries. It was the sow and she gorged herself by rearing up and helping herself from the dark green branches.

Despite the busy activity, Dildawn seemed an emptier place; the bats were hibernating, the snails had closed their firm doors and were parked together, close, in tiny caves between the trees. Slugs, too, were well hidden and many insects lay concealed in metamorphosis while their predators, the nightjars, had long since flown south to warmer climes. The air broke into a myriad pieces, frost poked down between grass blades and into the cold stillness sounded the two wide, moving shadows which never left the wood. The bank vole heard their calls, considered them to be too close for safety and with several urgently nervous hops, scurried to a well prepared hiding place.

Kewick landed near the ride and waited. An impatient woodmouse, more careless than her cousin farther up the path, pulled at a low-growing hazelnut. It came away in the tiny paws and, once tight in its claws, the mouse searched the surface, looking for a slight imperfection, somewhere rough and uneven to offer support to her upper incisor. Then she held the nut pressed against the ground, set it obliquely towards her own breast and began to cut a hole into the shell. Clouds moved again across the sky, bringing deep darkness, but Kewick heard the mouse. The creature sensed danger and froze. There was no second rustle to guide Kewick, but she did not wait for another clue; such was her skill, she had no need to delay her strike, but simply to change her normal hunting tactics. Instead of gliding out into the darkness, she beat her wings noiselessly in a head-on collision course with the mouse. Then, at the foot of the bush, within three wing flaps, she threw back her face, swung low her talons and, lifting high another meal, flew back to her perch.

Ule had drifted over to Alder Island and waited there as the boar badger moved along one of his well-worn pathways at the stream's edge. Where the bank dipped low and his path dropped down to water level Ule saw the badger pause and stoop, heard him lap noisily and drink. The water was icy cold and he did not take many mouthfuls. Above the sound of the rippling stream and the tumbling waterfall, badger and owl both heard a fox calling. It was a very small vixen, last season's cub, grown up and beginning to think of cubs of her own. The badger looked round, listened, sniffed the air, considered, then ambled on. Ule watched and listened as the badger departed and, distant on the light wind, came the bark of the dog fox; lithe, handsome, head down and brush held low, he was still in Longland, still hunting field voles.

The sky cleared again and there were feeble shadows against the remaining stars. One such shadow, of open wings, fell across the dead bracken and bramble; it touched the fox chewing noisily amidst the grass and he looked up. A tawny owl was hunting the frost-rimmed meadow. It was Kewick; she called to her mate, a questioning ululation growing faint as a memory. Morning was coming and in the burning cold, bank voles, brown rats and woodmice lay close, listening to the owls.

The hedgehog, too, prepared for the cold and for the day. Hard against a long, fallen log, under a tangle of bramble, the bristly creature collected leaves, half a dozen at a time, to make a pile. She snuffled, mounted the pile, scraped leaves towards herself, first with one paw, then the other. It was a big heap, ten times her own volume, and she pushed her way into the centre of the mound. There she heaved up the leaves and scratched at the ground, turning round and round, trampling the earth and leaves underfoot, working the rest into a pile to make a compact covering. It was a tidy arrangement, for the leaves lay like pages in a book, worked into layers by the comb-like action of her spines. So the hedgehog bid the night good day on the slope above Alder Island and, as her noises quietened, so Ule called again, but Kewick did not reply. She rarely called in flight, instead her wings took her over the derelict walls and quarry face, over the slope and the narrow arm of Longland to a roost, safe from the day; and Ule followed.

4

JANUARY SNOWS

The icy finger of winter pointed across the living skeleton of the deciduous woodland. An overwintering female brimstone butterfly, encrusted in ice, hung leaf-like from a bare twig. Other hibernating creatures had chosen warmer, less exposed holes and corners for their winter sleep, but there was no hiding from the winter for Ule and Kewick, they had to hunt on. So they perched separately, waiting for hunger to drive small creatures out of their dark hiding places into the keen danger of night.

The owls hunted successfully even in bad years because they knew every inch of Dildawn, *their* ground. Their sure knowledge of the terrain, its scrub and stream, its canopy and great trunks, told them where mole and shrew foraged their way under leaf litter, which trees yielded a harvest of nuts for rodents and, in the coldest times, they knew the warmest parts of the wood where finches huddled. Thus winter was theirs: nights, although cold, were long, food for small animals was scarce and cover, apart from noisy leaf litter, missing. Mammals in desperation became careless, and Ule and Kewick profited from their mistakes.

Night settled slow and long down the wild paths, shades advanced still and black through the trees, and in the bitterness of the cold night stars began to fall. Silent across the howling wind, a myriad, myriad stars, silver, falling perfectly, each shape unique. Through the air they came, glistening below the black blanket of night, wavering straight into the sullen waters of the stream and snuffing out suddenly, without

a sound. For two nights and a day the white air hung heavy, filling even sheltered corners with drifting ice crystals. On the second day, soon after eight, a large crimson sun mounted in a low arc over the wood. Ule and Kewick had been still all night and, although the snow had ceased to fall, they remained silent, unmoving on their perch, listening to the chatter of a bunch of hardy starlings bathing where the stream lapped gently at the edge of Alder Island. Some of the busy birds flapped up and hopped about in the bare branches, shaking off the snow, snapping their bills, mimicking jays, jackdaws, even the bleating sheep. And there were other sounds, despite the quietening effect of the snow. Trees and bushes talked, cracked under the covering of ice.

It was a glinting beauty. In the shadows white snow turned blue and dense thickets were purple-black against the dazzling ground. Everywhere was a poignant smell, the clean essence of snowfall hiding the damp musk of rotting leaves – a keen, lung-shrivelling aroma. But for all the beauty they were the difficult days, a hungry time. There had been no hunting. The two owls perched close and searched out the warmth and shelter of a thick ivy plant growing hard against the trunk of an ancient oak.

The day was clear, keen and cold, silent but for the laboured movement of a rabbit across the freezing ground. For nearly two days it had been imprisoned in its burrow; now it moved awkwardly along the woodland fringe, nibbling at sparse growth, searching for any tender bark. Suddenly it twitched nervously to a halt, listened intently to the harsh rattle of an alarmed crow. The bird had seen danger. Somewhere near there was a threat: a stark shadow against the sky. The rabbit stayed still. A buzzard flapped at less than a hundred feet up. The crow swung at it. The buzzard called, but its mews did not frighten the crow; it swung for a second time at the pride of Cloud Hill. The buzzard was almost defenceless, completely unable to outfly its smaller adversary. The crow was not concerned with defence, it was in search of a meal. By harassing the predator it hoped to force the buzzard to regurgitate the contents of its crop, but it was not to be; like all the other creatures of Dildawn, the buzzard, too, had gone without food for two long days.

All it was able to do was wobble unevenly on weak wings across snow-filled Longland, searching out any help from the slightest updraught of air, but there was none. The bird splayed its flight feathers as wide as it could, trying desperately to catch any thermal, and all the time the crow darted at its tail and head. The buzzard was chased all the way up Longland's quiet acres; then, far distant, up where the meadow joined wider pastures, within a swoop of Bendal's Bridge, a south-facing slope gave the buzzard the help required. It circled quickly on a narrow column of rising air.

'Kiew,' he called, 'kiew,' and 'kiew,' again.

The crow flew too, tried to splay its wings, but they were too narrow, no air current would lift them. So, while the buzzard glided up to the shattered sky where thousands of tiny ice crystals sparkled in the sunlight, the crow flapped wearily back to its warm perch in the tree. All this was unseen by Ule, but he had heard quite clearly.

The huge red sun burned through the day and down behind a dead elm. In the gathering eeriness there were other sounds. Tall ash poles rocked and swayed and, where one branch bore down upon another, they wheezed and creaked. A startled blackbird came swerving out of the withered sedge, followed by a pigeon. There was a distant shot, far away, but clear through the night air. Something moved down by the stream: it was the rabbit and it hopped miserably, breast-deep in snow. Breaking the thin crust of day it laboured hard across Longland's corner. Farther down a cock pheasant exploded out of the conifers, tail streaming behind it. A flash. Kewick winced. The shot sounded. Ule heard it and blinked. For a long moment the noise echoed across the stinging cold. Passing high and left the pheasant crumpled. Fell. Hit the snow. There were voices of delight. Human voices. A dog barked and lunged forward through the whiteness. Kewick lengthened her shape, merged with the mottled bark. There were more shots, moving westwards, meandering back towards the blazing log fires of Ston Gurney.

* * *

The vapours of night gathered over Dildawn. White flakes flew diagonally, for there was a slight wind, whispering through the larches. Another shot sounded, far distant. A late kill and the men and their dogs were gone. Ule stood up on his branch. He was uneasy. The shots had unsettled him and now the quietness – no leaves to rustle, no insects buzzing, just the wind, the cold, penetrating winter wind driving deeper, much deeper than it ever did in summer. Not a strong wind but sharp, keen into his roosting place. And the weather affected not only the owls, it added to the strain already taken by the trees of Dildawn. The ice and snow had been spreading their limbs for nearly a week. Where they were supple they gave, but one oak tree's lowest limb, twenty feet above the woodland floor, gave a long, horrifying creak, a tremendous groan through the white darkness, and broke off – the final stage of natural pruning, but a cacophonous interruption of night's stillness. Although it was dark, wood pigeons clattered through the trees, tumbled about the bare oak branches. Even Kewick was startled, but she did not move, just stood still and listened carefully as the quietness returned.

Bleak though the night was, there was some comfort in the deep, peaceful hush. Ule stretched his wings. Waited. Listened. There were bright shadows in the silence. Although it was deep winter, life was preparing itself for the coming spring. Kewick's calm, tremulous call reminded him. Not that either creature could afford to waste much energy in display, for neither had eaten properly for two nights, but they could sit and listen. And a distant sound came clear: the bark of a dog fox on the prowl. Ule looked, head bobbing, but he could see nothing. Silence returned and into it the eerie, gasping scream of the vixen. Ule followed suit, calling to his mate, and she replied, again and again, vociferous down the white-carpeted aisles of the darkness, while through the trees the vixen cried again.

As suddenly as they had interrupted it, so silence returned, hushed, muffled, almost complete; only the waterfall's mutterings disturbed, but those sounds seemed louder by the minute – almost a roar. It was into this emptiness that another call glided. Not Kewick. Not Ule. But Tawny. Another tawny owl calling out in that winter wood, in Dildawn! On the crags above St Stephen's Falls, high above Alder Island, there was a distinctive silhouette: an owl, moderately large but without ear tufts. A tawny owl come to find Kewick. An intruder looking for a mate, needing a territory. The invading owl called again and listened, hoped for a weakness in Ule's reply. If Ule's defence of Dildawn was hesitant then the wood would have a new lord and master of the night – a different tawny owl male – and after two nights in the freezing cold, without food, Ule was weak. The bold shadow called again from St Stephen's Falls. Ule heard him clearly through the darkness and called himself. Not to Kewick, but beyond to the night and its intruder.

A great loneliness fell across the wintry wilderness. Ule called again, with more effort, trying to summon up as much confidence as he could. Clearly he called and then he glided down to Alder Island, his ears searching, his eyes intent upon the cliff face above the waterfall. Silence. He was being watched, he sensed it and he called again. And the reply came quickly and close. Not from the waterfall, but out of a beech tree on the slope above the island, and the call was determined. It was a young owl calling, keen in the night air.

Ule turned to face the challenge. The half moon shone strongly over

the snow and the intruding call of competition came again. Ule did not reply; instead, with slow flaps of his silent wings, he flew to a neighbouring beech and there called clear and loud. On that branch he made obvious his image and emboldened his rights to territory by his formidable silhouette. Now there was no stopping him. He called again and again, and for the first time there was no reply but a scratching on a branch behind him; it had Ule turning almost clumsily in his haste. As he turned there was a call, close, clear and loud. Through the distant trees came Kewick's reply. To whom? Noisily Ule flapped his wings, disturbing snow in his energetic defence. Three icicles fell, splintering in ricochets from bare branch to bare branch.

Again Ule called, defiant. They were so close to each other that their bill-clicking seemed deafening, and from the stranger there came a moment's hesitation. Ule clicked some more, lowered his head and spread wide his wings. The intruder saw him, and there were long moments of consideration. He arched his back, but it was Ule who called out the final challenge. Kewick called too. She was much closer, for she had flown down to Alder Island.

On silent wings the invader glided between the pair, along the stream, up the falls, between the trees, across the cold fields and Hallow's Trow, over the empty road, to the oaks of Starvelark. Ule, on silent wings too, glided down to Alder Island and Kewick. They were together again, and they sat in the chill darkness, still and quiet, listening; but the invader had retreated completely and finally, left Dildawn for good.

It was a hollow victory, for although through ritual and display Ule had defeated a rival, winter was a greater danger. Unless he could hunt successfully, he would not live to outcall another invading male. Below the snow, protected by bracken, grass and bramble, the small mammals scurried back and forth along their unimpeded runs, almost warm, for the snow had kept out the frost. The owls' prey had disappeared.

Ule sat side by side with Kewick and considered the problem. And while they did so, the dog fox continued his song of love. The vixen heard him and encouraged him with her own replies. They were a pair. Their territories overlapped, but they did not live together. So, in that January cold they circled each other, coming closer. Yet the male was hungry for more than love. In the white darkness there was a rabbit. He saw it, nibbling at green bark on Longland's edge. The precise, elegant line of the fox's progress through the snow was distracted. At a tangent he began a circuitous stalk. The night was light, a half moon, Leo, Gemini, Cassiopeia; even the Pleiades, low on the western horizon, were bright, and the rufus coat was not so much a shadow as a walking advertisement on the damask meadow.

There was a flurry of ice crystals as the rabbit dashed for cover. The fox's own haste melted into blue-edged tracks. He paused and sniffed at the rabbit's leavings, the chaos of its panic and retreat. In frustration the dog fox marked his failure, leaving an orange stain on the snow. The vixen, wondering at his prolonged silence, called to him. He raised his head, considered and, empty jawed, moved towards her, but not without making a detour close by a pheasant roost in the holly trees. There, he hoped, a cold plump bird would fall an easy prey to his obvious stalking.

The crunch of the fox's padding feet faded. Silence returned to those few yards of Longland's edge, and in the stillness there was a slight movement in the bracken – a scuffling hop. The lucky young buck appeared timidly from the stop where he had bolted in the emergency. Then quickly he scurried down into the main warren, down to the bare earth to huddle against the warmth of his fellows.

*　　*　　*

The weather tested the owls' companionship. While rabbits and badgers slept warm in their holes and foxes dug with cold-bitten paws or sang songs of love, Ule and Kewick had to change their hunting ploy. Although specialist hunters of rodents, because their prey was hidden below the snow they had to seek out an alternative source of food. Ule flew off and Kewick followed.

Deep in her sett, the badger sow, though hidden from the howling cold, was active. She had scratched herself clean with great noise and fuss and now lay waiting, snuffling. Ule and Kewick might not be ready, but she was prepared. She carried in her womb the fruit of last summer's mating. It was during the long days of plenty and the warm nights of play that she had paired with her boar. The fertilised egg grew to the size of a pin head. A little bag filled with fluid, a small knot of cells, the future embryo, passed into the uterus. There it remained, joined by others, loose in that central space for the duration of fruitful autumn. But as the owls hunted in the frozen landscape, there was a silent pang of growth within the sow. Implantation. In eight weeks of lengthening days and shortening nights she would give birth. So with cousins, uncles and aunts about her, she rested, waiting for the snow to melt. The owls had no such choice.

Ule led Kewick to the hawthorn haunts. In the grey light she perched and waited. Watched her mate. Always in winter she stood on one foot; two feet on a frozen branch would have left her clumsy in talon, so with one foot warm and supple under her feathers, she waited on a successful hunt. There were many small birds roosting in the warmth of those bushes, and Ule knew it, as with uncharacteristic bustle he flew conspicuously down the line. Kewick waited the raucous seconds, then fell through the cold air onto one of those foolish birds disturbed by her companion. Her agility was amazing; although a large bird for those tight-growing bushes – her wing span was three feet – she twisted and turned through the branches of the scrub hawthorn without a sound, not one feather brushing against an ice-coated branch as she flew off to a night time perch with her catch.

Ule remained, still hunting, searching out his own meal. There were many there, almost within a talon's clasp. Pied wagtails, solitary hunters by day, had come together to sleep in each other's warmth. Usually they roosted in the reed beds, but the warmth of the water had been imprisoned by the thickening ice and so the cold forced them into the warm danger of the wood. Not all the birds had flown from Ule's first, frightening presence, many of them still hung tight to the branches, so he tried more violence. He beat his wings against the bush, hovered for a second, then beat again. And his wait was over. He too flew back to the eating place, and the wave of panic that had swirled through the hawthorns subsided, quietness returned.

The terror, the cold and the shock took a greater toll than the owls' talons; below those bushes there was carrion, blue and yellow. A silenced song. So light! It lay on the crisp snow without indenting the surface, and there were more: black and white, pink and long-tailed, dead, the flitting parties of the day cut down cruelly by night's cold. They had so little volume and such a large surface area that when they lost the little heat they had conserved they froze to death, toppled and plunged down onto the snow.

Cold the night and cold the air freezing around the vixen's muzzle. Below her thick pelt she was warm, but she paused to deal with one problem associated with the frost and snow. She bit at her front paw, pulling at a piece of ice almost freezing between her pads. Attention to her feet in that cold weather was important. If she hadn't kept frost and ice at bay she could have been lamed. So she tended her feet and all the while she heard her mate, but opportunist that she was, she chose to deviate from the path of love. She had heard the noise of panic in the hawthorn and knew what it meant, so she snaffled into the wake of the owls' hunting and found tiny birds brought low through fear onto the cold snow.

Throughout that long night cold and hunger drew them on. Both owls searched constantly for prey, and as night drew to its close Ule sat on his night time perch and produced a pellet. The ejected cylinder showed evidence of a less usual prey. It was almost cannibalism, for, after his visit to the hawthorn Ule had taken another, different prey – an owl. Cold and starvation had driven the little owl from its haunts of open farmland and its roosting hole and Ule spotted it on a sheltered fence post and took it.

Day came quickly after that eventful night, but night remained in the shadowed tell-tale tracks across the uniformly white blanket. The sky was bruised ochre and everywhere its light picked out the wild footprints, the tiny lacings of mice – some had, after all, surfaced in the dead of night, but all had escaped the owls' notice. There were no tracks anywhere of the badgers, for the whole family had lain up all night to live off their stores of fat, away from the cold. Rabbit tracks looped about the bramble thickets and bracken; near the holly tree were the three-toed markings of pheasant and, more sinister, the single-track spoor of fox. In the snow was frozen the midnight pounce, the feathers held tight by an icy grasp and, in a flurry of indistinct but deep markings, rose-pink stains. And yet in that same snow there were signs of spring. The trail of love. The dancing, weaving tracks of male around female – vixen and dog fox, alone in the snow – and the marks where she was laid low, yittering in submission to her dog; then, leading from that place, two parallel tracks across Longland – an elegant fulfilment of the night.

In the days that followed, the thaw came. It was a world of mists, a damp wilderness where the sparkle wore thin and bushes dripped. And as the snow fell to the ground with unnerving rustling and the runs of small mammals were revealed again, the owls were able to observe and to use these sightings to help them eat well and build up their strength for spring.

✻5✻

MARCH VIOLENCE

Ule and Kewick sensed the steady progress of winter into spring. The dog stars had swung westwards and fallen out of sight over the western horizon. Nights were much shorter. Snowdrops already trembled on sheltered banks, and at the edge of Longland the velvet-black smoothness of ash buds protruded into the clear skies of chill dawns. The night had passed quickly, although they had not been busy hunting, for now there were other considerations to take account of and the owls had spent many moments of the darkness singing a quiet tremulous song, one to the other. Gentle songs, long lasting and full of reassurance, sounds communicating thoughts deep with meaning and ritualised significance.

Not like the robin. As Ule and Kewick finished their night by flying over his land, back to their daytime perches, he burst into noisy song. A stranger was approaching his territory near the bridle path. He saw the intruder and flitted to the gatepost to sing a lusty warning. It had no effect. The stranger continued to feed and hopped nearer and nearer. The robin's song grew louder and longer, more insistent, but still it made no difference, for the intruder hopped over into his claimed territory.

All winter that female had defended her territory as fiercely as the robin was still defending his, but times had changed. Spring was coming in, even if the male had not recognised it, so when in his confusion he chased down from the gatepost and displayed his aggressive red breast, swaying back and forth, she ignored him – showed complete disinterest

in his posturings. Taken aback, the robin flitted to his song post again, to give another burst of vigorous trilling, but the female persisted in taking no notice of his attack; instead she hopped deeper into the defended territory and sang a brief song herself. It was a quiet song as she advanced closer towards him, and it perplexed him so much that he retreated from the unfamiliar, moved to a more distant perch and sang again. She flitted forward even closer and sang more of her song! He retreated yet again, but flaunted his red breast as he went. The song penetrated the dozing moments of the owls, but their day was punctuated by more than a pair of robins. While redbreast and his future mate tried to reconcile aggression and affection, male blackbirds were strutting about uttering their quiet, congested songs, right in front of their chosen female.

A mild south-westerly wind rustled through the bare branches, slightly ruffling Ule's feathers; shelter was difficult to find at that time of year, and during that morning the same wind rubbed against the beaded tassles which hung from the outer twigs of several ancient oaks on Dildawn's slopes. A golden dust – millions of microscopic pollen cells – swirled lightly through the air. Regeneration was beginning to fill Dildawn's early spring. Ule and Kewick felt it, heard it, sensed it.

Across the valley the rooks were busy, too. March was an important month for them. While the robin grew accustomed to the presence of his mate, let her move about his territory unmolested and became attentive to her, the rooks were putting the finishing touches to their nests. One male with his black wedge tail stood guard to stop colleagues pillaging his nest for the benefit of their own. Rooks are great thieves and the noise of squabbling and threats echoed round Ule's head. He turned to look in a half hearted way, but the rookery was a long way off; happenings there were silhouettes against the leafless skyline. But he did see one fight. The diligent owner of a half-completed nest had returned to find two idle thieves wrenching twigs from his construction. One flew off and escaped, but the aggrieved owner caught the other, gripped him tightly and, locked in combat, both birds fell to the floor of the rookery calling in dreadful tones. They wrestled briefly and then flew back to the remains of their nests to patch up the ravages of other thefts. And all the while Ule noted other rooks striding Longland, sedately twisting off dead grass for nest lining.

All day in the cold the owls waited, surrounded by the activity and promise of warmer months. The first wave of the new year's greenness moved imperceptibly across Dildawn's cool floor, right up to the entrance of an outlying earth. The dog fox was deep inside; not that owl or man would know, but he was there, warm and snug, nose buried deep in his brush, flicking his ears and listening just as keenly as Ule. They both heard the sounds: a lone hunter was about and there was the occasional dull pop of a gun. The fox lay tight, Ule and Kewick sat still. There was a long pause at this dusk. The fox waited and decided to delay his scavenging among the sheep. Such a decision might mean he would lose afterbirth to the crafty crows, but it was better to miss a meal than risk the pellets of that distant gun.

The sheep had been in Longland for five days – not that their presence made much difference to the owls. Their bleating seemed almost as constant as the murmurs of the waterfall, they noted the sound and discounted it. The creatures were huddled together in a tight flock, close enough to confuse a hungry predator, but loose enough to allow each beast and any suckling lambs room to feed comfortably. The hunter began to cross the meadow. A jay pecking about in the fallen leaves at the foot of the stile found what she'd been looking for – an acorn – and flew away in haste. Ule and Kewick watched, the fox listened and the flock stared after the green-clad figure and the long broken shadow lying across his forearm. The continual bleating filled the background of the hunter's mind, but his eyes searched the shadowed edge of Dildawn and its slopes.

A young ewe, full with her first lamb, had grazed her way out of the group. She saw the hunter coming and watched him intently. She was nervous at his sudden appearance. Suddenly she interpreted her own vulnerability and rushed back to the flock, disturbing several other sheep, the outmarkers, but the flock itself was undisturbed and continued to move slowly down Longland, towards the wider fields round Ston Gurney.

The hunter paused halfway across the field, and in the gathering gloom he clipped shut his gun. He looked about and started to walk again. Two long shadows, hard against oak bark, watched him carefully, but the owls were so well hidden that the hunter did not even sense their presence. However, there was movement at Dildawn's edge, where an old cock pheasant exploded suddenly from cover near the gate. It flew high over a tangled thorn to the right. The hunter swung round. There was a snap shot. The bird dropped and the owls heard the dying batter of the pheasant's wings flutter into silence, but it did not fall. The hunter was without his dog, so he plunged into the thicket himself to try to find the prize, but there was no bird. The old pheasant lay high, out of reach and out of the man's sight. After much noisy searching and shaking the hunter gave up, leaving the shot bird to the scavengers of Dildawn: black winged crows or, if the wind blew up during the night and was sufficiently strong to disturb the precarious carcase, chance might bring it to the feet of the fox.

With a sigh of annoyance the empty-handed hunter pushed his way back through the thorn and trudged the woodland edge, back down Longland, through the nagging noise of sheep, across Bendal's Bridge, to Ston Gurney and home. So sharp was his disappointment that he slammed shut his back door and laid his gun across the kitchen table before he looked up at his wife and smiled a weak smile.

A mile away, over the woods that saw his disappointment, starlings wheeled about the tall, straggling larch. Their noise seemed to have come from nowhere. Ule heard them and stirred. Began his evening call. Group after group dropped out of the rabble, like stones through the darkening day, their incessant babbling penetrating all the quiet ways. There was just enough light to show that some of the noisy birds were wearing their feathers thin. The white spangles of their autumn coats had faded into iridescent purples and greens, and some of the birds had exchanged the black bills of winter for gleaming yellow. Slowly the bustle and challenge quietened, while on the woodland floor the golden stars of celandine closed and the first thrusting spikes of primrose quivered. The sun set, and it was still the wind of winter which piped monotonously cold in the trees.

Close to a main trunk Ule and Kewick remained quite still. They were at ease, feathers fluffed up for warmth. Not even breathing betrayed their presence – as they inhaled the feathers were automatically drawn in slightly and then relaxed as they exhaled; to all appearances neither owl breathed, only at the lower back where the folded wings met could the slightest movement be detected. The robin sang on into the night. Although they were pleasant warblings it was a song of warning. Throughout the spring and summer he would often sing beyond dusk, just to ensure that no rival would steal his little patch of Dildawn. On that night, with a mate, he had a driving reason to protect his territory.

The owls' heads moved; with unblinking eyes they watched. Under the larch there was the slightest dusting of snow, and across it went a hare, on his well-worn track, back into Longland to feed. Everywhere there were signs of bustle. On the muddy bridleway the path was laced with the tracks of rabbits and with the lesser spoors of mice and tiny titmice, all signs of feverish activity. For Ule and Kewick it was different. There was a remote calmness about their life. All day they had heard the rush and fuss – robins, blackbirds and mistle thrushes singing fiercely – but they, the owls, had rested. They had relaxed and not allowed the bustle and noise to disturb them. Once only during the whole of the day were they tense, when a sparrowhawk darted in to take a careless thrush close by their perch. The plucked remains still lay on the woodland floor.

Ule stretched his wings. There was the rustle of a mouse. Kewick heard it. Hunted it. The first strike of night, and she swallowed it whole, as she always did. Ule was in no hurry, the night was long, so he gave a quiet and gentle display of song. Kewick replied. Her gentle mewing encouraged more notes from him. So they spoke to each other. For long moments they shared the darkness, then Ule flew off, down towards the stream, and his mate flew after him. She perched at a distance from him, on Alder Island about forty yards upstream, while Ule sat in a willow at the stream's edge. He was no more than five feet up in its bare branches, waiting, the constant murmur of the waterfall in his left ear, but there was nothing to see and nothing to hear.

Suddenly, nearer Kewick than himself, in the open crotch of an old tree high on the slope above the island, he heard a squirrel scrabble out of its drey. There were more scuffling sounds on the downward bark. He heard, and Kewick saw, the tail flow then stutter across the woodland floor. It was a steep slope above the owl, and the American grey squirrel, about eight-and-a-half inches long, was a big prey for her. So she called to frighten it, but let it escape, round the back of another dark tree. Ule ignored the irrelevant noises; he was intent on a chain of air bubbles linked across the stream. A water shrew was making its way towards the opposite bank, and as it did so it made a sudden troutlike jump on the surface – a pass at an early insect. Its last, for as it drew itself out of the stream on to its diving stone and began to clean its fur assiduously, there was the almost silent scratch of talons leaving a slender bough. So Ule flew to Alder Island, leaving behind an already unrelated, slight but continuing wave in the bare willow.

The wind strengthened; coming down from the north-east, it carried with it a certain dark, invincible something – a hoarse and eerie shriek, prolonged. From around the ruins of Kingwell Hall, Ule's white-winged cousin was calling. Although the tawny owl knew nothing of the barn owl's going, the sound evinced from him a response. He called loud and fierce, but Kewick distracted him with her gentle mewing, and from four wing flaps' distance he crooned back.

Across the valley, high on the slope near the old sandstone quarry, the moonlight caught the stripes of the boar badger. The noise of his sudden sniffing and then champing down a succulent worm frightened a nervous rabbit back into its burrow, to the intense frustration of the dog fox, unseen by both, as he stalked low, hiding his white throat and red haunches below the rusty bracken. The badger sniffed, champed and walked on, but the fox barked, snapped at his own tail, stopped to look up into the clear sky and saw the owl pair. Ule flew over him first, followed by Kewick.

It was an oak near the centre of the woodland which had attracted Ule's attention, and he wanted to show it to his mate. It was old, and fourteen feet up was a deep hollow – years before a limb had grown there, but it had died, rotted and finally groaned, creaked and fallen away. For years woodpeckers had come to drum and beetles to burrow, and after all that attention the hole had become deep and usable. Ule used all his skill at entering and leaving deep cavities to explore the hole. It was dark, dank and musty, but high and safe. It was a good place to leave from and a central place to bring prey to. He had found what he thought was suitable.

Kewick looked. It was important that they both agreed, both knew, so she dropped into the hole and shuffled about. To Ule waiting outside there appeared to be a moment's silence. Kewick was sitting still, considering, then she returned to the branch beside her mate and looked about her. It was secluded and easy to defend. With the tawny owl nesting is a discovery of possibilities, a decision, a choice, for they do not build a nest. So, as the hole was deep, two feet and more, and wide, with room to manoeuvre in and out, the work was done. They had chosen, that would be their nest site. Kewick flew off, Ule watched her go; they had agreed and so he followed her.

*   *   *

Dildawn was hushed, the sky open with the Milky Way crossing the northern horizon and the dog stars hidden from view. Even Cassiopeia lay low. Sharp into this dull night came the young vixen, heavy with cubs. Like the owls she searched for a ready-made hole, something to serve as a breeding chamber, and from her stance, her investigations, it seemed that it was to be high on the slope – she had decided to squat in an unused part of the badger sett. Almost slinking, she prowled through the night, probing the air with her nose. All around her was the musk of badger. There had been a mammoth spring cleaning, for the sow had had her cubs and they had fouled their bedding, so conscientiously the badger had turned out quantities of stale litter and replenished it with clean. Where the fox stood, not far from the main entrance to the sett, were piles of refuse producing the unmistakable scent, but the smell did not deter the vixen. She was not house-proud, not like the badger.

It was a curious fact that the badger had worked hard, not merely on renovating her own breeding chamber, but also a little farther away, on another chamber. She obviously had a reason, but these were not clear, at least not to the vixen, and so when she came upon the unoccupied hole she decided to take advantage of the badger's extensive digging. She went in carefully; nervously walked round and round and scent marked. Then she moved to the entrance. Sometimes a fox will share a badger sett. The vixen put her head out and smelt the night air. She stepped out, turned round, went back inside, made to lie down, but she was very uneasy; she thought she heard sounds outside, so she moved back to the entrance. Distantly came the call of Ule. Head bowed, the vixen moved forward to sniff the entrance smells. There was a loud snort. Suddenly a black shadow blocked her way.

Snapping flung her against the back wall of the sett. For two minutes the vixen screamed. Kewick heard her, the wood heard her. Then the cries ceased. There was a lull, then the quietness was broken by a stirring through the undergrowth on the slope, through the bramble and dead bracken: it was the sound of heavy dragging. Then the badger returned to her cubs. All around the body of the dead vixen were the footprints of a badger, yet there appeared to be no sign of wounds, no broken bones – but just around the neck of the hidden fox the fur was ruffled.

There were more screams that night, borne by the wind from the north-east – the barn owl still flew. Field and woodland were active, all over Dildawn's floor dark life crept and scurried. There were many reasons why Ule and Kewick should have been alert, but they were not. They had hunted well, fed sufficiently, and they now distracted themselves and the wood with their calls to each other. It was Kewick who took the initiative. She had attained her full maturity and there was more to those dark hours than hunting for survival. Inside her body cavity significant changes were pulsing, so she flew back to the old oak at the centre of Dildawn, close to the nest hole. Ule followed her and perched beside her on the same long limb. There was a moment's hesitation.

Ule watched his mate, saw her clear shadow through the darkness as she made known her intention. An age-old ritual began. They were a pair, but they were also individuals and predators; although they lived close to each other they never came too close. Beneath Kewick's soft billowing feathers lay the tools of her trade: killing talons and a cruel beak. Kewick was larger than Ule, but it was he who had to approach her, and with care. So he courted her compliance by swaying from side to side, raising himself vertically, lifting his wings and ruffling his plumage.

The plumage display went on, first a ruffling, then a compressing; Ule took on all sorts of shapes and sizes and as he did so he grunted. One moment he was an untidy ball of feathers, the next he was sleeked and tall. On that oak limb in the shadows it was clear that there was a conflict between approaching his mate and retreating from her. Ule made his advances slowly in ambling movements, watching Kewick's responses intently. Grunting, he sidled along the branch, moved closer, then hesitated and moved away again, with bill clicks and fuss. He was almost defensive, not at all the bold and confident lover. Timorously he moved forward, looking for the sign of welcome – trust was what he sought. Kewick postured, too, and there were tender begging calls. Ule came closer. Kewick uttered soft repetitive notes to reassure him, so inviting him to mount her.

After they had paired, they preened themselves; carefully, gently they leaned against each other, flank against flank, and tended each other's head plumage – such was their mutual trust that they used the weapons of death as the instruments of love. Several times in the lightening hours they came together, briefly, then they preened. Those moments were long and trusting. For several nights, while the badger cubs were licked into life, they rested and roosted close to each other, impressing each other with their bond of friendship and companionship.

*   *   *

In the days that followed their nights of love, yellow coltsfoot gave way to the primrose fleck and speedwell blue and deceiving dead nettle revealed its true nature with perfect florets of pristine white; at dusk squeaking starlings packed noisily into their roosts, preparing themselves for flight across the grey waters of the North Sea, back to the squares of Copenhagen, the parks of Stockholm, the dockside warehouses of Hamburg and the divided streets of Berlin. The fieldfare and redwing had flown already and were winging their way back to the forests of Scandinavia and Russia, looking for the sweet-smelling birch and pine forests of a cool, northern summer. The tide of migration had ebbed and now it began to turn and flow again. Distant Africa held million upon million of swallows and martins. They gathered at dusk too, twittering in their waiting lines, preparing for their warm journey over the sparkling Mediterranean, over the red-baked hills of Spain, back to the green, lush meadows of England. And all the while, as the month of March waned, Ule and Kewick were preoccupied, with themselves.

Despite the faint scent of growing grass it was still cold and in the long March twilight withered weeds were bleak along the stream's edge, rattling in the north wind. Dusk was busy: pigeons resorted to the oak tree to snaffle ivy berries, even mallard came hunting acorns and, despite brave efforts at song, along the bridle path blackbird and robin were puffed up and feeble. The pheasants sparred noisily at the woodland edge, their raucous calls and flashing colours drawing attention to their presence; rabbits watched with fascination as the heavy birds jumped and scolded at each other. Yet evening brought disinterest; the rabbits reverted to browsing and the protagonists strutted slowly back, with exaggerated importance, towards their roosts. Quietness fell. Across Longland loomed the darkening mass of Dildawn: the shadows of the wooded slopes became one as each tree fused into the whole. A white mist stole across the splash pool at the foot of St Stephen's Falls as the lingering twilight deepened into night. Orion's belt burned steadily, but low, in the west. There was the sharp 'wow-wow-wow-wow-wow' of the widowed dog fox, and Ule also called into the night.

Kewick sat on a favoured oak bough with a field vole, whole. She crushed the skull, then swallowed it head first. She had less than two nights' hunting left. A large ovarian follicle had burst and released an egg cell. It moved to the funnel-shaped mouth of the oviduct. There it was fertilised. Seeds of life were joined together and egg membranes were formed. Ule glided silently onto a branch close by, in his beak a bank vole.

Below them, clear in their vision, moved the large, shuffling shape of the boar badger, out on the prowl, snuffling down his well-worn pathway. Ahead of him was the familiar shape of another badger, but the boar recognised the intruder for what he was. He attacked, suddenly and violently. Over and over they rolled, biting and snapping with furious, stuttering growls. The resident boar released his grip, but only for a moment before closing in for a better hold. The newcomer was shaken, sensing defeat. He struggled furiously to rid himself of the pain and sharp teeth of his attacker, and rushed away, trotting ungainly as fast as he could, sliding out of the wood, over the verge and onto the road.

A sudden noise unbalanced the creature and, frightened by the nearness of the car, it turned to face the oncoming threat in its alarm posture. A futile, useless gesture. There was an enormous thump; a bang against hollow sheet steel. Brakes squealed. A car door opened and indistinct human voices approached: footsteps in the dead of night.

'What is it?' asked the woman.

'Can't really see,' replied the man. 'A dog,' he suggested.

'No,' she corrected him, 'look at his face.'

'A badger!' He had never seen one before, not close to, but he knew. He was surprised by the creature's size. It seemed quite big, out there in the darkness, living off the land without help, he thought.

'Poor thing.' His girlfriend voiced the pity.

'I didn't see him, not till it was too late. Did you?'

'Must have jumped out of the hedge.' And then he had another thought, more selfish.

'Where are you going?' she asked.

'To see what he's done to the front of our car.'

In silence they walked the few yards down the empty lane to the front of the car. The engine was still running, the headlights blazing. The car had caught the badger full square with bumper and number plate and ridden over him. The young man stepped forward, bent down, straightened out the bent plate, noticed a few hairs caught on the edge, and used his foot to brush them off.

'Hardly damaged us,' he said, relieved, yet remorseful. He moved towards the driver's door.

'You can't leave him there.'

'What?'

'The badger,' and she walked purposefully back up the road. He opened the car door and leaned inside to retrieve a pair of gloves. Nothing if not careful, he thought. Then he followed the girl.

They looked down at the mutilated body. 'It's not that far into the road.'

She disagreed. 'You've got to move it, poor thing.'

He looked at the stripes. Was it dead? He had seen dogs lie still with shock, then jump up and run away. It was not that he was afraid, just wary. After all the badger was a wild animal, strong, with claws and sharp teeth. He hesitated.

'Anyway,' she persuaded, 'it's a bit dangerous here, in the road, somebody else could . . .' and her words faded into silence. He knew what had to be done.

'All right. I'll – er – chuck it on the verge.' Carefully he took hold of the back legs, pulled at the broad rump, the chin dragged noisily across the loose gravel. Up near St Stephen's Falls the old dog fox barked.

'What on earth was that?' she asked her companion as he pivoted awkwardly round and tossed the corpse up out of harm's way on to the verge. To the girl the darkness was menacing. The distant sounds of life were portents of fear – so thin the veneer of civilisation, so powerful the influence of myth and legend.

'A fox or something,' was the reply, but he was rubbing his hands clean and hurrying back to the car, too busy to listen carefully and identify accurately.

Ule called, pure and clear, and the response in the humans was a flurry of uneasy thoughts.

'Come on, Adrian. Hurry up. It's very late. I've got to get up in the morning.'

So they climbed back into the car. Two doors slammed tight shut and, cocooned in their glass and metal box, with the familiar sounds of night radio, they drove off through the darkness along the quiet lane. Neither driver nor passenger saw the large square-winged silhouette, trapped for a moment in the headlight's beam. A bend in the road had diverted their attention and their conversation was of things that went bump in the night, but Ule shuddered in the glare at his remembrance of that time past, when a bright light was a whip and brought pain to his face. Silently he returned to a dark perch and listened.

Kewick was back on Alder Island. In her oviduct the egg-white wrapped itself round the egg cell. Although not conscious of those tiny movements of life, she sensed change. Her talons were still but open, grasping tightly at a small branch. Below her the stream fretted and gurgled in and out of tree roots and pebbles. The air was heavy; rain was coming in from the west to meet the advancing eastern light. The long minutes passed and, while Kewick rested, Ule recovered from his fright and flew to hunt again, but there was more significant movement deep inside the body of his mate: the egg cell and the albumen became covered in a paper-thin membrane and the shell was secreted.

The earth rolled over into damp day and, as the eastern sky brightened, Ule joined his mate at their daytime perch. Throughout the woodland blackbirds and robins sang heartily in wet shade; territorial rights had to be maintained despite the weather. Heavy drops of water clattered noisily around the resting owls. Glistening pussy willow catkins fell heavily wet to the ground and yellow celandine lay clenched tight shut in the gloom, obstinately waiting for the clouds to lift and the sun to warm the woodland with its low rays. Only the primrose was open to the dank weather, its gentle colour woven about with fresh green goose grass, growing strongly.

Morning came and the owls were still and silent. Distant from them along the wet road to school, a small child paused at the roadside verge, looked hard and long at the dead badger, but did not touch. Instead she muttered: 'Poor thing!' something she had learnt from her mother Then, sadly, she wandered slowly onwards, into another day.

6

KEWICK IN HIDING

The springtime sun finally came to Longland. The meadow was bathed in its rays from morning until the chill of dusk, and all that time the thin wailing of newborn lambs wavered across the valley bottom. The wobbly legged creatures were thirsty and urgent and the ewes were patient, but the sheep were not alone. In the fading light of that spring evening, small shadowy shapes moved through the cropped grass. A dozen brown hares had raced out into the open to join in the annual congregation. During the long dark months of winter not one hare had been seen during the hours of daylight, but in that golden light they jumped and boxed – clear silhouettes against the green sky. Groups stood about in the daylight, seemingly uncaring of danger. They were upright on their haunches, forepaws high off the ground. The bucks showed off, while the does ambled about, stopping to feed or smell a patch of ground.

There was the sound of leather flicked across leather. One buck stood up against another and there were more blows, fur flew, the boxing match continued. Others played follow-my-leader, two or three bucks chasing one doe; wherever she went they followed; whatever she did they did. Never hurrying, always in line, one length from each other, they wandered through the maze of courtship, the procession weaving in and out. There was another boxing match and then they all browsed. For several minutes they fed, moving slowly and erratically across the meadow; then suddenly a buck kicked out violently and another ran in a circle, leaped sideways a good three yards as if his paws were scalded on hot coals. Another strong-thighed buck did even better, jumped four yards, stopped stock still and began twitching, shaking his forepaws.

The chasing and the leaping continued, then the males made passes at the females, leaped over the does and squirted them with urine in an attempt to mark a mate; finally, one by one, the bucks fell back onto four legs, sniffed the grass and browsing resumed.

In the centre of Dildawn Ule stirred. All day he had rested on a branch just above the nest hole. It was the first time that they had roosted in that oak tree. Kewick had decided and flown to the spot, and Ule had followed. Night was coming and Ule shook his wings and called gently. There was no sign of Kewick, all the branches were empty. Ule called again, quietly, almost tenderly. There was a shuffling inside the dark hole and she scrambled out of the nest. She was hungry.

Around the owl pair the woodland floor began to rustle and bustle. For several nights, but unknown to the owls because they had not been near enough, a young male woodmouse had emerged, blinking, from his tiny hole down at the side of an old stump, and scurried over towards a fallen bough. It was quite a big limb, brought down by winter's storms, and already the bark was flaking off and the wood rotting, attracting insect life, so the little animal had fed well. The tiny creature scurried and probed nervously and noisily, his ears constantly alert, searching the night for sounds of danger. Like all mice he was shortsighted – unaware of distant shadows – and Kewick was that shadow looking down from her waiting perch. The mouse moved forward in delicate hops, wary but hungry, scratched with a forepaw and was exposed, unprotected from the wide wings and snatching talons. So she stalled her flight into an upward climb, leaving a small feather on the woodland floor, and returned to her night time perch. There, as always, she crushed the skull and swallowed.

The sky was clear and cloudless, stars pricked out in lavish profusion. Towards the east, high above the waterfall, Leo sparkled. The dog stars hung low, but the Plough was still there, almost directly above the wood and the meadow; because the moon had five more orbiting hours before it would rise over Dildawn's slopes, there were few bold shadows. Away from the stream, snuffling through a hedgebottom near the boxing hares, was a thin, hungry, female hedgehog. Urgently she looked for food, feeling the spikes of frost sharp among her own prickles. Having awoken from her winter sleep her metabolism was high and she needed to feed well if she was to fight off the cold of the night. To survive the season she must build up a layer of fat and acquire enough

energy to produce young, should she find a mate. Ule saw her scurry across the bridle path; her questing nose was cold and the ground was beginning to harden up. He was on his way down to the edge of Longland to wait and listen.

Once he had alighted and settled himself with little fuss and less noise, he searched the night for its sounds. Dismissing the shuffling hedgehog as irrelevant he tuned into another commotion, down at the woodland edge. He bobbed his head to take in the strange sight: a stoat dancing, somersaulting about. Ule looked on in wide-eyed curiosity. Although a naturally playful animal, that stoat was about something much more serious: making use of the natural inquisitiveness of other creatures to aid his hunting – an unnecessary ploy, for the chosen prey was a week-old leveret lying up in its form. A brother and sister lay quietly in other hiding places, separated by their mother for safety's sake. They had all been born with wide-awake blue eyes, full fur and the ability to walk, and their mother had encouraged them into widely distant milking forms soon after the birth. So all three leverets waited for the mother to do her round of maternal duty. The young creature trembled in the deep moss on the slope at the edge of Dildawn. It sensed danger.

The four-legged predator ran up close and pounced. There was a pitiful scream. Hares browsing in Longland heard it. One female dashed with leaps and enormous strides to her offspring. She leaped over the stoat, kicking him with her hind legs as she passed, knocking the hunter sideways. The stoat rolled over a little but immediately sprang to his hind legs, making a threatening, ginnying noise. The mother hare approached him carefully, making sinister, low, muttering sounds, stamping her back legs on the moss. The stoat argued back and the leveret uttered a weak wail.

Without warning the hare rushed at the stoat with punching forelegs; taken by surprise the creature ran off and hid in an old rabbit warren which lay empty and disused nearby. At the entrance to a crumbling burrow he menaced the doe with spits and noisy threats. The mother hare returned to her young one and stood over it, licking the leveret's back once or twice. The young creature was still alive, although it had a fearful mark behind its head – deep skin punctures. The stoat began to circle the pair, at a distance, staring in frustration. The hare stood her ground and after several moments the stoat decided to slink away into the undergrowth. For long minutes the doe waited, staring at the spot in the undergrowth where the stoat had disappeared. Her ears were alert, but as long, uneventful moments passed, she crept off too, through stems of dog's mercury, back to her nibbling companions.

All the while, silent, Ule had watched and waited. As soon as the doe moved away, he glided down to the mossy bed and lifted the quivering, wounded creature – one predator's loss was another's gain. Not long afterwards the stoat returned to find the form warm but empty – the prey had flown to feed another's need. After sniffing the ground once or twice, checking that the leveret had not crawled away into another nearby hiding place, the hunter moved off, following the interlaced scents of other small mammals.

At the nest Kewick stood at ease on a broad branch and stretched her wings. Apart from the glide to catch the woodmouse she had not flown at all. Tight to the trunk she had waited patiently. She moved along the oak limb and called to her mate. The reply came distantly through the trees. Ule was down at Longland hunting for himself and so should she, for she was hungry enough. Her ears searched out the quiet darkness. There was a bat about – the first of spring. Kewick heard it clearly. The tiny creature had woken and flown down from the quarry face to hawk at Longland's edge, so there must have been night flying insects about, too, perhaps an old lady moth. Reluctantly Kewick left the oak tree, flew to Ule at the meadow's edge and perched close to him. The whole of the night had passed and Kewick had sat it out; she badly needed more food. There were moles about in Longland's grass, male moles fighting. The female owl hesitated, then unfurled her talons and opened her efficient beak. It was a tough prey, but it was a meal; she swallowed, eating her second meal of the night – hardly sufficient, and yet still she was curiously inactive. Only Ule flew, returning frequently to sit next to her.

Deep in the night, as the light brightened with the risen moon, she moved off. Morning was only minutes away and a greater spotted woodpecker drummed out his territorial rights: eight blows to the second. Clearly Kewick heard them echoing round the flagstone cliffs. She had gone down to Alder Island, but she was not patiently watching and waiting. If an owl could fidget, that was what she was doing. Her oviduct had secreted the mucus to expel the fully formed egg. She called. Ule replied, but he did not go to her side. She called again and her talons scratched quietly on the bark as she dropped from her temporary perch and took an urgent low flight to the old oak at the centre of their wood.

After she had alighted and perched comfortably, she called to her mate again, then she looked at the hole. She examined it and considered. She listened and watched. Looked all around her. And suddenly without warning she disappeared, sliding down into the nest. At the bottom of the hole she shuffled into a convenient position and a white, almost spherical egg rolled gently over the slight slope and rested against the heartwood of the main trunk. Her first laid egg. It was about forty-five millimetres in diameter and smooth, with only a faint gloss; here and there on the surface were small chalky lumps. She snuggled over the egg and above her head there was a scratching at the nest's entrance. Ule's wide-open face peered in. He was watching her. His talons slipped on the oak's armour plating. He trod air, made firm his grip. Kewick looked up at him. The owls shared the moment – a gentle tremulous note – then she shuffled slightly and her mate flapped off into day.

All along the woodland edge blackthorn's snowy stars were bright against bare spiky twigs, and lower in the hedge bottom another constellation sparkled yellow – celandine. The male tawny hooted. The sound echoed round Longland. Distant from Dildawn's centre came a muffled reply. Then, swiftly, to avoid the mobbing day, Ule flew back to the oak at the centre of Dildawn and perched just above the dark hole. There he slept, bolt upright, hard against the trunk.

The day awoke. The moon, though still high, was a ghost of itself, for the sun was bright with spring. A yellow brimstone butterfly flittered through the bare wood. Normally she would feed on buckthorn, but it was not feeding that lifted her, on that warm morning, high into the air: a male attended her. He followed her fragile climb, determined, both of them, gold in the blue of day. A breath of air held her for one short moment, then down she tumbled in a steep dive and hid herself in some thick ivy which smothered an old sweet chestnut; the male dutifully followed her into its sheltered depths.

The owls snoozed on, although the stirrings in Dildawn were noisy and from time to time destructive. The elastic-sided nest of a long-tailed tit quivered and shook, but not with life; it was a magpie come to destroy. The bird broke open the exquisitely woven creation in his search for eggs. It had taken a fortnight to build – all the artistry of the female tit, all the hours of the male, fetching and carrying moss, birch bark, lichen, even cobwebs and cocoon silk, reduced to this, the magpie's frustrated greed. The nest held nothing, neither eggs nor chicks, so the marauder flew off empty beaked, leaving expensive litter on Dildawn's floor. Usually the long-tailed tit will lay early, before the leaves come, and magpies know the shape of their nests, but for some reason that bird had come into season late. On that morning her first egg was ready, but her nest was not, and down one of the woodland's sunny rides there came a trilling 'tsimp, tsimp'. The owls paid no attention; there was just the slightest movement on their facial ruffs, the feathers moved a fraction out of place to receive more clearly that urgent signal – a long-tailed tit suffering from the predation of the day. The tit had to lay her egg somewhere, so she found a damp bed of moss, laid the tiny pea-sized sphere and wasted it. Inside her tiny self she resorbed the developing ova and with her mate reverted to an earlier task – nest building.

A squirrel had watched her closely and seen it all. As soon as she flew off he moved forward, picked up the dull yellowish-white egg and nibbled, profiting from the magpie's greedy destructiveness; and as he ate another yellow brimstone fluttered by.

The air was clear and dry. An early bee bumbled about searching out the first nectar-bearing blossoms. Lapwings, distant, ran and winked through the sky, above a warm brown field close to Bendal's Bridge. A male flew up, displaying, demanding his rights. Up he went, slowly beating his black and white wings, climbing steadily before twisting into a rolling, headlong dive. Then, in a blur of wings, a flurry of buzzing beats, he defied gravity and twisted upwards again.

Throughout the day there was busy activity – the lambs found their feet and the sheep were protective, and the buzzards were back, circling high overhead. But Kewick was still, deep in her hole, snuggling over her egg. The long March twilight came. An early pipistrelle flitted out from behind the ivy, safe from the owl's hunting talons, for Ule was not quick or agile enough to take a bat in flight. Kewick did not attempt to leave her hole. Ule fidgeted awake and called, but he knew that hunting was now his sole responsibility. He had to hunt for himself, for Kewick and later, when the egg hatched, for the chick too. So he stood up on the branch, flapped his rested wings and flew off, down to Alder Island. There he waited and listened. High on the slope above the stream he heard a violent scratching – the hedgehog was out and about again.

*   *   *

It was an average year for rodents in Dildawn. The hunting was good, but not easy. Not like the year before, when they had been a young pair and hunting was much more difficult. It had been a severe winter and there were few mice about. Kewick had laid two eggs and waited in her nest for Ule to bring his first catch of the night. She was hungry. For three long hours she had waited and he had not come. An east wind had carried the chimes of distant Hallow's Trow Church, it was eleven o'clock. Kewick did not know the time, but hunger had forced her out

and away from the nest, to hunt for herself.

If only she had waited just a few minutes more. But she had not. She flew off at eleven o'clock and at five minutes past Ule had returned with a field vole dangling from his beak. It was for her. He had called gently, a muffled call for his mouth was full, but there was no answer. He scratched at the nest entrance. Still no Kewick. He looked inside. The nest was empty! Curious, he had tumbled down into the hole. Two white eggs lay at the bottom and, as he stumbled in the darkness, his talons struck out and smashed a delicate sphere. All the effort, all the hope, halved in one foolish moment. Ule had stood there in the sheltered darkness and listened. For twenty minutes he had waited in that hole, the shattered egg oozing at his feet, and still there was no Kewick. So he had swallowed the vole himself and flown away.

For an hour and a half Kewick had hunted and fed herself that night, then, long after the chimes of midnight, she had returned to her nest. She had paused at the edge, sensing that something was wrong. Somehow she knew that there had been an intrusion. Owls have a poor sense of smell, but the scent of her own egg was strong on the night air. For several moments she had considered, hesitated, looked about, but finally she dropped into the hole with its broken egg. For four confused hours she had shuffled about pecking at the broken remains. Then, at a time when Ule might have expected her to appear for feeding and wing stretching, she came out of her nest and flew away. She never went back, not to that hole, nor to the tree. It was a lucky squirrel, exploring the oak, who found the second, cold egg and broke into it. So it was an odd sort of summer for the young pair without owlets to look after. They had stayed together, lived off the scarce prey, but their loyalty had been tested.

*   *   *

So it was that in this second breeding season they had chosen a different nest hole, away from the site of the first disaster, and yet in this new spring darkness Kewick waited again, and again was hungry. She called again, and her voice travelled thin but clear through the wood's whisperings. Ule heard it as he hunted in Longland. There a field vole had been careless and he snatched at his first success of the night. Yet even as he grasped his prey, an impatient Kewick called urgently again. She was ravenous. Ule did not reply, he flew direct and silent back to his mate, with a long tail dangling untidily from his beak. Once at the oak tree, his mate accepted the gift hurriedly; nervously, in protective zeal, she despatched her mate and swallowed the prey. Then she slid back into the nest to snuggle over her first and only egg.

From a nearby perch Ule stared at that hole, then around at dark Dildawn. Kewick had left him, left him to the night. Slowly, in perfect silence, he flew back to his hunting perch above Longland's edge. The hedgehog was already there, her sharp teeth breaking into a small snail. There were noisy crushing gruntings and the licking of satisfied lips followed by a quick shuffle and a twig turned over. A scramble of woodlice scurried away but a succulent slug met its fate.

Ule listened and heard another sound. It was approaching in an ambling but methodical way. The boar badger on his night time pathway came close to the snuffling hedgehog; she listened, sniffed once or twice, tensed herself into a ball and rolled into an awkward pose down the slope. Although the badger was intrigued, and although some badgers have a way of skinning the prickly animal, he left well alone.

The woodland was full of noises. Behind him Ule heard a scurrying through an oak tree. It was the stoat, bird nesting. Almost like a squirrel it ran about the branches, jumped across to a neighbouring ash and clawed its swift way to the ground, then moved away towards the rabbit warren – a slick, silk-brown movement, rippling through the grass, intent in every step. So the night was watched by Ule but ignored by Kewick; she sat still, almost silent, and so it was for the next day and night.

Early in the third morning of her incubation, Ule came to the oak tree and called. There was no reply. He called again. Still there was no reply, so he moved to the nest hole and looked in. Kewick was there, panting. She looked up. Her second egg rolled gently against the warmth of her feathers. Another three days and three nights followed and then her clutch was complete.

*   *   *

Leo, from its position in the southern sky, moved slowly east to west, sinking down the western horizon; Arcturus and Corona Borealis ascended; Vega was strong and bright. These names were known only to the humans who looked up into the April sky, like the woman at Greyfield; but Ule, without naming, knew, saw the stars move round the season and felt the month warm with life. And Kewick, all the while, deep in her nest hole, was almost sedentary; only at dawn and dusk did she come out to stretch her wings and take gifts of food from her mate. For the rest of her time she cared for the clutch, gently lifted and turned the eggs. Several times a day she carried out that chore and then settled back down over them, making sure that her brood feathers packed tightly round the three white spheres. So she kept the eggs warm and Ule, alone in the wood, kept Kewick fed. Reassuring calls between the two birds were less public, less frequent and much quieter.

But their bond was secure; instinct, duty, survival of their species, those were the considerations which bound them close together.

The process of life's growth continued. Inside the yolk sacs of Kewick's eggs the germinal discs divided, first one egg, then another, over a period of six days. To everything within those eggs there was that sequence, in order of laying – three days separating each. So the embryos grew, fed on the yolk and came closer to birth. Through thousands of pores in the shell, oxygen entered and carbon dioxide filtered out. Life in that dark warmth took on a recognisable shape, just as life in Dildawn's day bloomed with its accustomed beauty: rich dark umber, young sunshine gold on old trunks, gossamer on the wooden gate, and the sunshine again, threading through its bars – mellow. Everywhere the colour of spring: a thousand shades of green. And in that spring sunshine there seemed to be more than the countryside responding to the lengthening days. It was in Ule's hardworking eyes and in the beak of a starling as he carried a dandelion to his mate sitting on their nest.

Late one April night, as the scurrying, scuttering woodland floor whirred back into hiding and Ule fed his mate for the last time, there was slight panic. Kewick had swallowed the bank vole and returned to her brooding confinement, and Ule had flapped out to circle their tree before settling down into the camouflage of day. The dawn chorus had been loud for nearly an hour, when a different song cut across the open woodland. In the brightening day came the distinct cry of a male owl. It called again. Ule was startled, he feared another invasion. Dildawn was vital to him and his family. He responded immediately, called out in full confidence and flew off into the early morning to show himself and find the threat. Unknown to him a jay had abandoned the gurgling of its own song and for no apparent reason had imitated to perfection the call of a male tawny owl. Urgently, but in complete silence, Ule glided up over the waterfall, along the bridle path and across Longland. All the time he flew he searched, but could find nothing, just a raucous jay flapping out of the wood and across the fields with a derisive 'scaaaaaarg'. He perched on Alder Island, looked up at the waterfall and waited. Long moments passed by, deep into the day; still he watched and listened, but there was nothing to see, nothing to hear. After a long time, when he was quite satisfied that the threat had passed by, he gave a last call to the bright day and flew back to his perch above Kewick and their eggs.

*　　　*　　　*

The golden flowers of celandine bloomed their way through the hurrying days of April. Snails explored the fading blossoms of the dying flowers of spring. Swallow Day spun onward towards the Day of Primroses. Life's pace quickened and, although no swallows came on their appointed day, early that morning, flying low, almost brushing Longland's growing grass, a male cuckoo came skimming over the hedgetop. For that moment he was silent; neither of Dildawn's cuckoos advertised their presence for a further three days.

Life was bubbling everywhere in song, in colour and in scent. In the owl nest the warm attention of the female continued. The eggs were carefully tended. The fragile shell hid the dense white, protecting the vital sac, as did the opalescent spirals of albumen cord, one from either side of the yolk, buffering it from shock, helping to keep it in its central position when Kewick turned each egg. Dildawn's green sea spread and with it the buzzing days. A queen bee, red tailed, bumbled large and unhurried through the sunshine, collecting bits of dried grass. She took the pieces to her underground nest – a hole left behind by one of Ule's victims, a woodmouse. For two days she worked hard. After she had finished her nest building she went collecting again – for nectar and pollen – then she returned to the mousehole and made her bee bread, placing it in the middle of her nest. With all her preparations completed, she laid her eggs and covered them with wax. In the damp gloom, day faded, night filled out and she rested, and while she slept, tucking her head under her foreleg, Ule hunted, and when day came and the owls slept she made her foodstore: honey; unlike Kewick she had no mate to feed her, but like her owl counterpart, when all was done she incubated her eggs.

The long chorus of April swelled. Dimpsey was full of song, and into the wide fields came the call of the male cuckoo. Ule heard it, but there was more to dusk than the cuckoo's first call. Within her warm darkness Kewick heard a faint cheeping. Her first laid egg began to talk to her. As the shadows lengthened and faded there came a gentle tapping on the shell, from the inside. The sounds filled her dozing moments, and the female owl cooed back, quietly. Mother learned her baby's call and baby owl learned her mother's voice; and Ule, when he brought fresh-caught prey, heard Kewick's cooing, different, though familiar; when he flew back into the night he hooted. For no apparent reason, he called a long, confident note.

APRIL MORNING

The twenty-first morning of April. The twenty-ninth of Kewick's incubation. It was still and cold. White patches of mist clung loosely to the branches of the oak trees. In the far darkness, over a distant field, a skylark rose in song. Man's earth was quiet, not a chainsaw, plane or car interrupted the clear perfection of the warbling melody. Slowly the lark climbed, two hundred feet it rose into the lightening air, then at the peak of its song it sank, down to the ground.

In the grass, the eye of day, pink edged and white, lay tight shut against the parting of darkness's curtain. Massive oaks, sentinel and black, without a leaf to quiver, stood still. Bats flittered from them and, as the wood fell silent, there was a faint tremor, a slight stirring. All night the egg had quivered; inside, the tiny chick with its head under a wing, had wriggled round, chipped as hard as it could. The egg tooth on the owlet's small beak was breaking a neat circle in the white egg. Kewick fidgeted with uncertain expectation. She called her mate, and he returned with his last catch of the night, disturbing a pair of crows who awoke in frenzy. Rooks, more distant on their nests at the woodland edge, joined in with their softer notes, but soon the early morning quietness returned. In the nest, however, it was far from still. The egg tooth continued to draw its blank circle on the blunt egg, from inside.

The crack grew, a tiny piece of shell fell away, and when the circle was all but complete, the tiny incarcerated creature began to stretch and push hard against the fragile obstacle.

The woman at Greyfield was up and about. It was eighteen minutes past four and she was stooped, looking down at a series of rat droppings in the roadway outside her cottage. Some time during the night a colony of rats had passed by. Where they had gone it was hard to tell, but she had her suspicions: her own outbuildings and grounds. The dawn chorus distracted her. That was her reason for being on the road, to listen, and she straightened up in admiration to listen to her local thrush out-rivalling its neighbour with a full song phrase. A new day exploded with the five-second 'tit, tit, tit' of a wren singing from an exposed perch on the thick ivy. Then a blackcap joined in with its rich chorus. So the darkness of the morning built up to a crescendo, while the stars of celandine and wood anemone brightened and sparkled in their full, bold colours. A mud-spattered boar badger trundled by to his sett on the slope after a night of feeding on juicy bluebell bulbs. The sun shone brightly.

The woman returned to her kitchen, and in the owl nest the neatly chiselled cap broke off, the egg opened and out of it came the first of the clutch: a tawny chick, bedraggled, exhausted, but alive. It was just an ordinary miracle in the early morning of that day in spring, but as the explosion of song faded into the business of day, Kewick cosseted and comforted the newborn with a soft covering of her own feathers.

Helpless, blind and nearly naked, the tiny chick was completely dependent upon her parents. In a sense it was birth time for the parents, too. All three of them, adult owls and nestling, had new roles. For the chick it was the formidable task of learning and, most difficult of all, acquiring the skill needed to be a night hunter. For Ule and Kewick there were new routines, new stimuli; when awake the chick snorted and gobbled, strained and groaned, waved her head about as though casting an invisible net. The parents watched her, their first of the season, and found in her early strangeness a family face. That open beak might have been brand new, but it was aeons old in instinct, and it was that gaping bill which dominated the night-long caring of the adult owls. The sound of Ule, or his shape at the nest hole, was enough to start her greedy head nodding, her gullet gaping.

So the night was long for Kewick, though short in darkness, for there was the impatience of her young chick, the first and only born. She transmitted the chick's longing for food by calling to Ule. He was hunting on their behalf, so he did not reply. Instead Kewick heard another sound: not far from the nest hole, on Dildawn's growing floor, a courting hedgehog couple were growling and churring at each other.

They were nose to nose, but the male hedgehog had advanced too far, too close for the female's liking, so she cuffed him and he backed off. He tried again, but she snapped at him and tried to bite his nose. He paused before trying a third time, but still she rebuffed him, so he changed his tactics. He began to trip round her, almost light on his stubby legs, and as he went he panted and hissed. The female held her ground, pivoted round on the spot, spitting and hissing back. He circled more closely, but it was too close because she cuffed him soundly across the nose. Once more he backed off and started to circle her in the opposite direction, and all the while he made his noises of love and she responded with seeming aggression.

Distant on his hunting ground, Ule called, and Kewick replied. For a moment the hedgehog male seemed to give up. He ceased his noises, but it was of complete indifference to the female; quite nonchalantly she turned away and began to search for food. Again he tried to court her. Clockwise and anticlockwise, snuffling and hissing, churring and spitting, while the male owl winged over their courting, a circling shadow.

As he approached, Kewick heard Ule's soft call and came out to meet him. He alighted, close to her, not on their oak tree, but on a more distant chestnut, and Kewick snatched the mouse from him and sent him away as quickly as she could. He was a predator, and as a caring mother she feared for the safety of her young one. Once Ule had flown away she returned to the nest and tore the prey into digestible if gory portions, gave the feeding call and the owlet swallowed greedily.

Meanwhile on the woodland floor the hedgehog sounds were becoming quieter. Although the churring continued the female had turned her back on her hedgehog suitor, but she had also laid her spines flat; so without ado he mounted her, and all the while he grunted and groaned, panted and churred. The owlet finished her first meal, and the hedgehogs disentangled themselves. They backed away from each other and shuffled off across Dildawn's mossy slopes, in opposite directions, leaving behind them quaint circles in the dark: a central depression where the sow had pivoted, a circular track about one foot in diameter where her hind feet had pushed her body in the circle of love, and at a further distance, out of range of her snapping teeth, an ill-defined groove where her boar had circled her in both directions during their hour-long courtship.

Within three nights another chick was born and Ule was kept busy, for Kewick called impatiently from the nest telling him of the hunger of their two chicks; he was forced into daylight hunting and began to disturb other nesting birds. Each time the small birds of the day heard his quiet 'kuwit' of approach, they broke into fearful alarm calls, and the more he hunted in the light of day, the more frantic became their alarms.

However, if Ule was constantly irked and irritated by small birds, so his mate, deep in the nest, was also plagued by smaller things – flies. The young owlets fed very clumsily and Kewick was not well practised at tearing prey into pieces; so the nest floor was littered with morsels of rejected food, and round it, in the warming days, flies buzzed. Kewick did her best to disturb them and frighten them off, but it was useless. When the noise and the buzzing became more than she could bear, she bill-clicked noisily, and soon the two sisters learned to make the same sound.

So another three days passed, and on the third day after hatching her second chick, Kewick felt the last egg quiver. It began to talk to her, as all her eggs had done. And as the egg talked, so Queen Red Tail, the bumble bee queen, safely ensconced in the hole excavated by one of Ule's rodent victims, hatched her own brood. Another of her tribe was not so fortunate. That bee, red-tailed also, bumbled down to the stream, right into a pebble, the collision forcing it over onto its back and into the water. Helpless it swirled, wings inundated, along the stream. For several moments its sedate progress seemed charted into doom, but another piece of flotsam collided with it and the bee climbed onto the twig and held tight. An eddy took hold of the twig and swirled it round and back, hard against the grass bank where the water held it still; so the bee returned to dry land, dragged its drenched body into the sun and let the process of wing drying take its course.

Although its antennae were stretched out, its head was crouched, buried deep down into the grass, and its raised abdomen pulsed in pants. Around the small drying body flitted tiny midges. The bee seemed tired, almost lethargic, for all its movements were slow and laboured. There were no wing buzzings as the delicate cells dried and no flight away from the stream when flight was possible. The creature simply clung to the grass, just eight inches away from the rushing waters, and moved its head slightly to the right; there they were, a group of parasites, just over a millimetre long, wax coloured with long antennae for their short bodies. A few had crawled around to the pinched space between the thorax and abdomen: bee mites.

And there was worse, internal parasites – ichneumon grubs – driving the bee to distraction's edge, back into the waters of the stream; and that second time, fortune and the current were less kind. Out towards the central flow bobbed the bee and on the furry body there was a rushing as a dozen, dozen legs scurried minutely onto the top of the hopelessly drifting form. Just one drama of a day which broadened out in the owl nest into the sound of a chipping shell.

The whole of the day was busy and quick, full of new arrivals. A dull-coloured bird flew by, very close to the ground, only a few centimetres above the grass of the meadow, its wings barely above the horizontal line of the body. It could almost have been a sparrowhawk, but it was not, it was a female cuckoo. An early female scouting the hedgerow looking for nests, for although she was not ready to lay she was preparing. Ule flew over her and Kewick, out of the nest for her short evening wing stretch, called. It was dusk, and darkness and the sounds of night disturbed the unwelcome migrant; she flew down into a depression, low all the way into dense cover to hide away from the dark hours.

Short night deepened and Ule visited the nest three times with an offering, then flew away, down to Alder Island. There he heard the rhythmic, steady padding of the boar badger's feet, along the path, over the rocks at the edge of the stream down to the water's edge for a long drink. The black and white head went straight to the water's surface and out jumped a large frog. It startled the badger, but he grabbed at it. He took it uneasily, but there was a slip between paw and jaw and the frog escaped with a plop back into the stream. There it scurried for safety at the bottom. The badger tried to give chase, but the frog hid himself well, leaving the hunter to paw the surface and sniff in a bemused trance. After several moments of consideration the badger reverted to drinking, and when he had quenched his thirst he idly turned a stone over; but on each turning he was disappointed – no frog jumped out to frighten or distract him.

Ule flew over the badger in the stream; he was also looking for a distraction, a rest from the rigours of duty, and he knew where to find it. He flew up to St Stephen's Falls. The falls were thirty feet high and cliffs around and about them more than doubled the height of the enclosure. It was a damp and hidden place; a series of broad steps carved out of the flat-bedded sandstone rose up from the stream bed. The rocks there were never dry; damp, slippery moss clung close to them and the continuous wash of water had pitted the rock faces with shallow depressions. These pools were filled with a fine spray thrown out from the main body of the falling stream. In his eagerness to enjoy the cool dampness, Ule landed with less than his usual caution. There was no place to take claw hold; his legs splayed, his wings flapped and unceremoniously he rolled down and across into a shallow pool. There was a tremendous flapping and splashing. He was wetter, much wetter than he had intended, and wet without the enjoyment! He flew up to a dry pinnacle of rock at the top of the cliff and shook himself, almost like a dog; then he was damply still.

For long moments he sat with his head at a considering angle, eyes penetrating the darkness, taking in the full view of the tumbling stream, ears straining above the sounds of falling water; but he could neither see nor hear anything of importance, so he preened. It was a favourite place, that waterfall; both he and Kewick had spent many moments of damp darkness there, but on that night he was alone, more alone than he had been for many a long night. Around him were the moonlit wood and the shadows of night.

A slug rasped slowly through the grass, its wavering tentacles eager for the scent of food, its respiratory pore open wide, breathing deeply from the night air. He grabbed at it; a small morsel, but he swallowed. More damp moments followed, but the night air was dry and his feathers were soon preened back into flying condition. He looked up and listened, then he leaned forward, tumbled down the rock face, swooped low over the splash pool and up over the rock-strewn pool, across the zebra-striped bridle path, where the branches and twigs cast clear shadows, and down onto a hunting perch. Kewick's call had reminded him and brought him back to duty.

The dawn chorus was already establishing itself in full song, although it would be another half hour before Dildawn benefited from the sun's light. Deep in the wakening wood, Kewick lifted herself out of the nest and flew a short distance to another oak; she could still see the nest hole and protect it, but she needed to exercise and also she needed to greet her mate, but in a safe place, away from the nest. On a third tree, distant from her, a blackbird sang in the morning and, competing with the sweetness of his song, came the calls of two hungry female owlets. Kewick heard them and called again to Ule, and he replied with a soft approaching 'kuwit'. She went out to meet him, took the field vole and despatched him yet again to Dildawn's brightening depths while she returned to the nest. There she scrambled into the deep hole and gave the feeding call. The two chicks responded with excitement, drowning out the tiny sounds of chipping. A hole in the circular crack which ran round the end of the egg had grown large enough for a small beak to protrude. The third chick, a male, called to the world outside. There was more chipping and the crack was almost completed.

As the cacophony of the dawn chorus began to quieten, Kewick left the sleeping owl sisters and flew across to deposit another pellet at the foot of a nearby oak. There was no sign or sound of Ule who was still hunting, so she sat on a branch and dozed quietly. Into this calm erupted the third chick; he heaved hard against the cracked cap and broke suddenly with great effort into the nest, emerging as a bedraggled heap and waking his siblings. They were already hungry again, and there was a great difference in size between the first-born and the wet heap of hardly living flesh, but before the elder chick could interpret the newcomer as food, Kewick returned and snuggled over her latest born. She was faced with a new problem: protecting her third chick from the other two, because, unless there was a steady supply of food and unless she was constantly alert, it was likely that the third-born would be eaten by his sisters. She shuffled about to make herself and her new chick more comfortable, and called to Ule. The owlets had to eat again before the inactivity of the day took over from the business of the night. Through the wood Ule heard the call and with tired wings flapped back to the nest, carrying yet another meal, the last of that night's shift.

*   *   *

May dawned. Blossom was upon the branches, new buds snapped open; on Dildawn's slopes ground-hugging mists of bluebells gathered, while other single blooms, fragile against immense trunks, struggled on in shade. In the bumble bee's domain the first workers had emerged and were busy collecting food for themselves, for their queen and for subsequent broods. They buzzed about the woodland floor carrying great loads of pollen almost a quarter of their own weight, hauled from red campion to bluebell, from wood anemone to celandine and back to their nest. But while the workers bumbled and probed, buzzing about the woodland with legs dangling, there was a different sound close to the old queen's mousehole. Workers in the nest recognised a hairy intruder, but the heavy skin of the invader protected her from the aggression of the defending bees. Their stings seemed to do no harm to her at all. The invader overpowered the rightful queen and installed herself within the nest.

So the cuckoo bee usurped a throne and, during the growing days of spring, the workers had to learn to tolerate her newly established presence, just as local dunnocks had to learn to feed the insatiable appetite of another invading parasite: the cuckoo, or rather her egg, and the subsequent chick.

In the hole in the old oak the shapeless little bundles of soft grey down began to thrive, bustling clumsily about the nest – all eyes, beaks and claws. Above them was the day, lit by the exploding sun, with swifts and swallows weaving bold patterns in the sky. The swifts especially, with their screaming, sailed round and round, strong winged, pairs searching each other out. The owls heard them as they swept upwards, higher and higher, until one bird, the male, dropped onto the back of another, the female, and both sank down together, falling through their piercing shrieks. They had travelled thousands of miles to search out Longland and its rising insects; indeed they had been on the wing for nine well-travelled months, not touching the earth's surface since they had left the meadow the previous autumn. With noise and aerobatics they created a new season's family and came down to earth to lay eggs in the rafters of Hallow's Trow and Ston Gurney.

With the screaming of the swifts and the opening of their beaks and the parcelling up of a myriad insects, life reached upwards. Weeds of warm green light thrived everywhere. And a precise pronouncement of this annual blessing fell with a breath of light onto Dildawn's floor. A single dandelion seed, blown out of Longland's ground, parachuted down to start its life in Dildawn's shade, an invader from the meadow. There the tiny ribbed seed pierced the brown littered earth, balanced precariously and waited for root and crown of flower; just as the owl chicks waited for food, fuel for their own growth and maturity. Already they had a tinge of adulthood. At the edge of their stubby wings there was the slightest trace of owl feathers, a suggestion of the future, and on their tails the same suggestion in scalloped lace. The tools of their trade were well formed, almost a caricature in creatures so young – a large beak and strong well-covered legs above full size talons – but their faces were really no more than down, hardly a feeble white line to indicate the characteristic saucer shapes of the tawny owl.

But there were other signs of growth. The milky-blue eyes of babyhood were turning brown and their effectiveness was improving by the dark hour. During the first few days after their birth they could just pick out movement, but as the irises took on the colour of adulthood they also acquired the function-keen night sight. It was that sight on which they relied for survival. Not their own, but that of their father. The hunting was good, but that was not the same as easy, and, often as Ule hunted, there were long waits between feeds. During those waits, and during the heat of the day, the owl nest was quiet. The chicks slept and Kewick rested her head at the edge of the hole, but for Ule there was very little time for sleeping. With four hungry mouths to feed, as well as his own, he needed at least a dozen catches a night and because dark nights were short, he had to hunt more and more into the day. Almost anything would do – beetles, even worms – but even indiscriminate hunting stretched Ule to the limits of his considerable endurance. Kewick sensed it, too, and from time to time she went out into the night to help him by hunting for herself.

As the month progressed Ule was tested more and more. His skills as a hunter were put to trial time and again. He knew Dildawn's untidy slopes well – fallen boughs, the rotting stumps, the living ways, the hidden paths, places where the patient wait and the silent glide were usually rewarded, and he knew the other places too, where sometimes there was a chance of prey. He also knew the law of the opportunist. He never discounted any possibility, always investigating any sound or sight which might lead to prey. Thus he hunted. His methods were energy-saving, for by waiting quietly he did not consume the reservoirs of strength which hovering or soaring demand. But tense, alert concentration did not come without its own cost, and hunting into the unfamiliar light of day also drained his strength and gave him insufficient time to recover. And overwork was not the only danger, for when he searched for food in the alleyways of the day there were other keen-eyed hunters, bigger than he, hunters who might take exception to his poaching in their preserves of light.

* * *

Early one morning Kewick returned to the nest with a small field vole. The second sister snatched the prey and took the creature in her beak. The owlets were now sufficiently mature not to need Kewick to tear up prey; instead the owlet jerked back her head and snapped forward, thus wedging the vole's head firmly in her beak. She jerked again and again, leaving only the tail dangling from the right side of her greedy bill. All the chicks ate like that, taking the prey whole, in enormous gulps; to grow they had to eat well, and so, just as Ule was urgent in his hunting, they were eager in their eating.

That day young rabbits browsed the long bright morning at Dildawn's quiet edge. Ule had one of them chosen. From his perch he had stood up and prepared himself for the glide forward. He was aware of the daytime competitors, but that was the risk necessity forced upon him. He flew out of the wood with his talons spread, and as suddenly as he left his branch, so came also to Longland, out of a down draught, the familiar but menacing mew.

'Kiew.' So high, almost unseen. 'Kiew.'

The mewing of the Cloud Hill buzzards. Their eyes had scanned the land for prey and one dropped low. Rabbits ran for cover. Instinctively Kewick and her owlets, though well hidden, were still and, pressing their plumage close to their bodies, stretched upwards, assuming a long thin posture, not a shape a predator would associate with a tasty meal. Those short seconds were long with action. While an unconcerned bee continued to collect pollen from a dandelion, the buzzard's shadow fell across the climbing sun and came down onto the meadow with its whistling silence: strong wings through the warming air. The predator struck well.

'Kiew, kiew,' and again, 'kiew.'

Effortlessly it climbed out of the wooded valley – wide circles of ease on a rising thermal of hot air. Slowly the bird spiralled upwards, fading out of earshot, into a high and silent movement, wide wings above the heat.

Kewick did not see the buzzard go but she sensed its passing, for the world about her reverted to its normal business. Tits began to search again and young rabbits browsed, and there were butterflies – speckled woods in shades where the undergrowth met in tunnels overhead, and brimstones where the sun was bright, and also, sunning itself on a fresh green leaf, a green-veined white. Dildawn was back to normal and Kewick called to Ule, a call of relief, a call into the day. There was no answer. The flies in the nest were becoming a nuisance again, and so were her chicks. They were hungry and insistent. She called again and still there was no reply. She waited. In distant Longland a magpie clung tight to the back of a sheep, digging deep into the wool for ticks.

Kewick called again, but Ule did not come and there was no reply, only 'Tchackertchack' from a thieving jackdaw feeling threatened by the unusual persistence of an owl's cry in daylight; he flew off to a different place to find his food – fruit, insects, carrion, he was quite omnivorous and keen eyed, too – and he found what he was looking for, close to the old wall. It was an old hedgehog. Somewhere in the darkness of night, three weeks ago, it had felt the pang of death and had moved to the warm shelter and hidden itself in comfort, to die. For three long weeks it had lain there, unseen by large-scale plunderers, but a myriad writhing maggots bore witness to the attention of other, smaller pillaging bands, and seeing the white grubs erupt in greed, the jackdaw fluttered down to strut and peck at fresh meat, turning putrefaction to advantage.

For Kewick the hour was still empty. She knew that there should be no waiting for owls in the morning light, but fighting her instinct and her distaste for the sun, she clambered out of the nest and shuffled about. She head-bobbed, blinked open her night time vision, trying to interpret the fierce shadows of the day. There was no sign of Ule.

Silently she glided away from her young ones. Flew past the nests of screaming birds – her entire progress charted not by any sound she made, but by the squawks of the fearful. On she travelled towards Longland, flying quietly to his perch at the side of the meadow, but he was not there. Longland was strangely empty. The sheep grazed and bleated, the rabbits browsed and twitched nervously close to the safety of the woodland margin, but her mate was not to be seen. She swept onwards in her search, circling slowly the familiar acres, scenes of shared experience, places of earlier joy. There was no Ule – nowhere his familiar shape. The air was empty of his cry. She was drawn back towards the nest.

Distracted from her usual quiet flight pattern, suddenly she flew like a rocket out of the trees, cut Longland's corner, terrified a pied wagtail and hurtled back into Dildawn where she stalled her flight, turned her feathers slightly so that the air rushed past the vanes, making more noise than a startled pigeon. Birds exploded from every bush, pigeons clattered, even a jay flew high, back over the larches. She flew onwards, back into a silent glide through the dappled shade, across a small clearing, and she saw him – his body on the woodland floor, silent and motionless. Ule! His talons firmly clasped a young dead rabbit.

Kewick glided down and alighted as softly as one of her own feathers. Ule was caught in an open ray of sun, his eyes tight shut against the brightness, but he heard her. She head-bobbed, looked closely at him and hopped forward cautiously to his side. She called softly and he stirred into weary movement, shook open his wings, recognised her shape, released the rabbit and hopped back. He was worn out by diligent care for his family, and choosing a very heavy prey so late in the hunting night had been a miscalculation. Although Ule had managed to drag the dead creature some distance from Longland, it was obvious that neither he nor Kewick could carry it back to the nest; as they rarely tore their prey to eat it, by mutual, but unspoken consent, they left the rabbit for others. Kewick flew back to the nest and Ule, with long slow flaps of effort, found his daytime roost. He had to rest, hide from the day and prepare for the night.

8

MAYTIME HEATWAVE

Nothing seemed to move. Sparse clouds hung silently from the blue haze and there was the drowse of heat. Slow-moving snails had climbed stems of grass, trying to escape from the reflected warmth of the heavy soil. Cattle crowded in tight shadows hard against Dildawn's edge, raising a singing cloak of flies with their tired tails. Long hours had passed since the cool of dawn and in those moments was the smell of the ripe earth, and animals seeking out shade.

Even in the green heart of the wood, the hot sun had made life in the nest hole almost unbearable. Kewick had been forced out to find a cooler, more airy perch in a high tree. There she leaned close to the trunk, but her sight lines were clear, right through to her brood. The chicks were alone in the stuffiness of the nest, panting and shuffling about, trying to shake off the flies which clung close to the decaying food left everywhere in cracks and crevices. Above the irritating buzz other sounds cascaded into the darkness of the hole: grasshoppers piped treble, distant dragonflies bassooned over the stream and close by a speckled thrush sang loud, long and rich. But in the nest it was all buzzing and discomfort, and the sound of almost despairing bill clicks.

All the owlets curled their tongues, snapping them from the roofs of their mouths. Click, click, click, click, a rapid series of small explosions of irritation. For long, uncomfortable minutes the three owlets clicked, panted, clicked and panted, stamping about, attacking the flies with their stubby talons.

Suddenly the clicking ceased, their breath was stopped. Echoing through the pillared emptiness of the wood came the sounds of a noisy, invading herd. The sun had brought the human visitors out across the fields to Dildawn.

They came, trampling through the dappled sunshine of the weekend. A blackbird spotted them first and raised the alarm with harsh, persistent 'pink-pink-pink-pink-pink-pink-pink-pink-pink' down the ride, through the glade, right past the oak and on, through increasing agitation into the safety of deep undergrowth. The family that bustled so noisily did not even notice the fleeing bird, they were heavily laden and intent.

'There, Bob,' pointed mother, and father dutifully took out the polythene sheet. A jay chased a magpie over the ride and into the trees, but none of the humans saw them.

'Not there, dear, over that stump, so's your dad's got summat to sit on. You know, his leg. He can't get up and down like he used to.'

Father moved the polythene, repositioned it.

'Ah! That's better,' approved mother and looked about her as her son rushed up to her.

'Mum, this place ain't no good. There ain't no room.'

'Of course there is.'

'Mum, there ain't. Look. All these logs an' trees and things. I can't play football here.'

'Stop whining, Darren,' shouted father, frightening a patient wood pigeon from its perch on a nearby oak. 'Just go away and explore for a couple of minutes. It won't be long before your mother's got the food ready.'

The small boy turned sullen and kicked away at the grass and spring flowers.

Mother bustled about inside her polythene bags and an attentive daughter helped.

'Dad!' called father to an old man, his own father. 'Come over here, sit down and have a rest.'

High above them and distant, Ule and Kewick watched and listened, paying close attention to their strange, erratic ways. Indeed all around that small family animals waited and watched. Unknown to the humans the day was heavy with scents – relics of the night when badger and fox marked out their temporary territories. Only the family dog smelt the signs, but even he did not understand. Mother and daughter prepared busily, taking the food out of the bags: the box of jam tarts, the aluminium foil cases, the packets of crisps; out they came and down they went, once emptied, onto Dildawn's growing floor, to mark uncaring, unthinking human invasion.

Over a year, few people came to Dildawn, but those who did usually left more than their fading scents. The calling cards of civilised man were cartons, spent cartridges, empty packets and cigarette stubs. And true to habit they were there on that day; no sunny weekend would have been the same without them. So the humans sat down and fed. Then the adults rested. Father had a slow pipe, mother had a quiet doze and grandad rambled through his memories of times past when every day was long and hot and walks were winding, full of scent and views of dappled sunshine, when wild animals were tame and easy to see.

All the while the humans picnicked, Ule was still and Kewick perfectly silent. They heard a distant buzzard call, a sound which passed the human ears by. To the visitors the day was full of a wash of meaningless drowsings, but the impatience of the children finally invaded the plans of the adults. Darren had thrown too many sticks and the dog had sniffed and anointed so many foxy-smelling bushes that his leg was tired, and quiet Vanessa had finished her pretty necklace of threaded bluebells. She was very pleased with her idea and got up to move across the clearing to show grandad her handiwork.

'Here, let me see,' and her brother ripped it off her neck. 'Oh, sorry, I didn't mean to.'

But Darren's contrition did not contain her caterwauling. The owlets stirred. Kewick looked down, moved her head slightly.

'Darren, you come here,' called his exasperated mother. But he was full of youthful guile and called back to his sister as he ran away, 'Vanessa, Vanessa, come quick, look – a squirrel! A squirrel!'

'Where?'

'There. There on the path.'

'Oh yes. Mum! Mum! Look!'

In three bounds the creature was across the woodland floor, running from the noise; up the far side of a tall tree it scratched its escape route and then sat and watched. The picnic broke up. Father got to his feet, sighed and banged out his pipe on the heel of his shoe. Mother tossed a final chocolate wrapper into a bramble.

'Well, what shall we do now?' asked father, stretching and yawning, feeling full and wholesome.

'Back to the car,' whined Vanessa. 'Otherwise we'll miss children's tele.'

91

'Can't you do without the tele just for one day?' asked her mother, made testy by the heat.

'Yes, it's nice out here, better than back in the stuffy old house,' added a conciliatory grandad.

'Come on,' said mother, sorry that she had been so sharp. It's a nice day she thought and the family ought to enjoy it. 'Let's pick some bluebells. Like the old days, eh, dad?' And her husband's father smiled back.

'That everything?' asked father, and they moved off, uprooting armfuls of bluebells as they went. Ule watched but Kewick seemed even more alert as the noise of the humans approached the old oak. Grandfather leaned on his walking stick and Vanessa held his hand and chattered. The old man enjoyed listening; the sound of the young voice pleased him. His own son excited the dog into stupidity. He had the idea of throwing a broken branch and the dog willingly chased after it and slid through a carpet of spring flowers, barked and jumped at the thrown stick. A pheasant suddenly broke cover and flapped noisily into a towering flight over bramble and into dense hawthorn. The dog snapped back, but it was too late, and it gave a half-hearted chase into the bushes, snicked its nose on a thorn and hurried back whimpering to its owner.

The boy had run on ahead and his mother called to him to slow down and wait. He was no naturalist although he was observant in a different kind of way, and he spotted the oak tree. It was inviting. Very tempting because it seemed easy to climb with its fissured trunk and spreading boughs. Ignoring his mother's distant warning, he ran forward and jumped at the lowest limb, swung up and started his climb. He was very pleased with himself and shouted back in triumph and pleasure.

Ten feet above him the young owls' feathers froze still and their heads rotated. The flies still bumbled about their feet but the young birds were silent and still, their unblinking eyes gazing intently at the nest hole entrance. Their lopsided ears picked up the deafening clumsiness of the young human's brash adventure. On another bough, well camouflaged but watching him intently, sat Kewick, and out of the warm afternoon came the sudden, silent explosion of her fury. She had to defend her nest and she struck hard at the boy's head. He screamed but somehow managed to scramble down the tree, grazing his shins. Kewick wheeled on her agile wings, preparing to swoop again. But there was no need. The family was ordering its retreat. Mother had dropped her bags and was comforting her son, looking at his head and legs. Grandad was waving his stick in a forlorn sort of defiance against the bird, while father had leashed the dog and was picking up the fallen picnic bags. So the family hurried out of the wood, disconcerted and in some ways afraid, not realising how lucky Darren had been; many who have interfered with a tawny owl's nest have lost more than composure – eyes are a favourite target.

For a few moments after their departure the wood seemed unusually quiet, then an owl bill-clicked. A blackbird returned, flew down the ride and across the glade but in silence – there was no alarm to announce. A pheasant bustled and strutted, undisturbed by a distant car engine starting up. On the woodland floor lay a broken branch crushing a small group of wood anemones and twenty yards away from the oak was an untidy pile of bruised and dying bluebells, all that remained of a Sunday afternoon's walk in Dildawn. And Kewick was back on her perch, dozing, but listening attentively to all the noises of the day.

* * *

The year broadened. A mayfly dried its wings on a warm streamside pebble. The woodland buzzed with bees bumbling about from branching blossom to flowering floor. The woodland edge was alive with song and birth. A wagtail ran across the grazed pasture of Longland with whirring legs almost invisible, as it chased to catch a fly. The buzzards still circled, the cuckoo still called and inside the owl nest hole the owlets grew fast. Their moments were busy with movement, eerie rehearsals for reactions they would rely on later in the year. Random movements, out of sequence but exact, automatic but strangely knowing. Although they were merely big round bundles of dirty white fluff and large red-rimmed eyes, they were firmly established as tenants of the old wood.

Their big clawed feet scrambled about the hole and the oldest chick shuffled to the rim of the nest hole; she blinked roundly at the sun and jumped. She fell fourteen feet, flapping her all but useless wings. When she landed her first instinct was to scuttle for cover, but she hesitated, turned and jumped about a foot up the trunk, clawed desperately with her feet and beak, her wings flailing about as she tried to climb the tree with a frantic urgency. She reached upwards about a yard, then fell back to the ground, an untidy bustle of feathers panting and scrambling. Above her, the second chick tottered at the brink and, startling a chaffinch by her ungainly entry into the wide, wild world, plummeted down to join her sister, trying to use her wings to cling to the warm air and thus break the fury of her fall. Then both owlets attacked the trunk, with talons, with pecking bills and much flapping of their wings. So, by great effort and determination the young pair climbed back to a perch some nine feet above the ground, not too far from the nest hole.

It was all part of the great plan – their preparation for life as night hunters – but rain interrupted. A storm cloud burst with a low close rumble and teeming rain. Close to the nest, Kewick called out to reassure the adventurous chicks and called again to try to encourage the third owlet to leave the hole; but he ignored her, and continued to sit tight in the stuffy dryness. She called again, but her last-born would not be tempted into the dripping wetness. To emphasise her insistence, Kewick dropped back into the nest; she shuffled busily and called less softly. There was a sudden flurry of feathers and wings, a noisy scratching and an outburst of bill-clicking and the reluctant chick was hustled out across the bark and on to an open, wet branch.

For a full hour all four owls sat huddled, hiding from the drips, and as lightning flashed the owlets blinked from the brightness and bill-clicked nervously. The charged air was full of strangeness and it was also full of day. They looked about them and waited. It was a short storm and faded away beyond Starvelark's oaks in less than an hour, leaving Dildawn's air smelling fresh and allowing the animals of the day to leave their hiding places.

Although the day was far from ending, there was a heavy, darkened look to the wood. Leaves filled the air, blotting out the sun, but on more open ground not far from the stream, amongst the tall sedge, a blunt nose twitched: the harvest mouse was out and about again, exploring the damp slipperiness of tall grasses. The stream continued its babbling, although those stones, out of shade and water, baked hot in the high sunlight. On the bank, in a cool spot, a fat water vole sat on his well-worn doorstep of mud, chewing noisily at green sedge, smelling the rich moist scents of thrown water and rippling currents. A drowsy torpor filled the hours. Down along the streamside jungle, where the land was flat, there was an undecided splashing. Cows had wallowed into the shallow stream, trying to wash flies off their legs and flanks. They stood squat and still, moving only their tails and their square, pink mouths.

Inexorably the day and the sun fell across the bright sky, full of the sound of fingers rubbed across glass – the piercing screams of hunting swifts. Rank smells rose as the sun sank: nettles, elder and drying grass. Open light left the top of the bush and, as the first star of night appeared in the turquoise blue, a greenfinch hopped about, searching a night time roosting place. The clarity of the day wore thin as the stars grew in brilliance, and the owls began to move, slightly, silently but with increasing intent. Very cautiously a woodmouse crept out and peeped through stems of grass.

A light breeze blew across Longland, so gentle that only the ripest dandelion clock succumbed, though in that late daytime the pasture was full of the fragile spheres. The whole air danced with tiny wisps of light – gnats illuminated by the low sun, each minute creature with its own halo of light. The bridle path was full of ploppiting rabbits and the air above glistened with seeds, pollen, bees and hoverfly, but in the darkling wood, an unseen shadow moved.

Kewick began to preen herself. Her feathers were worn, so she sat and carefully jettisoned a couple of inner primary feathers. They fell lazily through the long light of evening. She watched them, then looked up and across. The woodmouse had long since hopped away, but a small group of young rabbits emerged in a cluster, looking curious and uncertain. They browsed. One grazing animal leaned forward, just as he had seen his elders and betters do, his throat flat to the ground, and rubbed his scent gland up and down, his chin rasping against the grass.

Kewick stood up, alert. A blackbird pinked down a nearby ride. The owl did not glide but danger of a different kind came stalking. A big cat, a tabby cat, a tom cat. Kewick saw it. A nightjar churred through the scented twilight, up and over the darkening conifers. Ule heard it, saw the flitting shadows of the bats, hawking open-mouthed along their night time paths. And still the cat came. A noisy shrew screamed in the dense centre of a thorn thicket, safe, racing along its regular path. The cat stood still and stared ahead. Two young rabbits, motionless, close to the bramble bush, their fur fluffed up, came into his focus. He put one paw forward, then another. Another blackbird shrieked, shot out and the white tails bobbed away. The pounce had missed its target. He shook himself and walked across to the oak. The owls were uneasy as the cat raised himself onto hind legs, his forepaws digging deep into the bark. There was a long sharp scratching, but having sharpened his claws, he moved off, following the remaining scents of the day.

As the cat walked lightly through the shadows, he identified a peculiar movement. Ule saw it too. He head-bobbed, his eyes searching the woodland floor. There were six grunting shadows circling, trotting round in an arc a dozen feet across. The cat decided to stalk again, approached carefully and close, recognised the spines and from previous experience decided to leave the six trotting hedgehogs alone. So Ule relaxed and the cat went on his way, but the hedgehogs continued with their circular tramplings. Kewick too had been watching and she made

sure that the cat was well out of Dildawn and well into Longland and the hidden grassy runs of field voles before she relaxed. With her chicks not long out of the nest she was unusually wary.

Ule followed the cat down to Longland, saw the creature leaping with success into a clump of long grass quite close to the stile and chose a distant perch. It was not long before he returned to the nest. Kewick saw him coming and became quite agitated; she took his offering quickly and despatched him well away from the perching chicks before she distributed the first meal of the night. The oldest chick was the lucky recipient but the sight of food set the others off into a pandemonium of demands. They were all hungry, so Kewick left them and flew down to join Ule on Alder Island. As soon as she left her chicks they quietened down, knowing instinctively that without their mother, noise served only to attract danger.

High on the slope, at the badger sett, there was a slight movement. A black and white face fidgeted at the entrance. A nose extended upwards to read the night's scent which passed slowly over the twitching snout. There was a moment of decision, then the old boar crept out and waddled down the slope. In a few steps he had reached his dung pit and squatted with his tail raised. That done he returned to his usual place close to his own front door and began to claw at his fur: under his chin, then the back of his neck, then over on his back with his hind legs and tail spread out, scratching furiously at his underside with both sets of claws, one at a time. After many minutes of this noisy grooming he got up onto his four flat pads, shook himself down, and ambled round to a different part of the sett to investigate the sow's living quarters. He stuck his head in and gave a greeting, a deep-throated purr, then, behind first, he backed out into the night to wait. It was a long, long wait and he fidgeted about. First he stuck his nose into several interesting corners, then he went back to the entrance and called again, less gently, but there was no reply. The sow was in there all right – he could hear her – but she would not come out, so he decided that he would wait no longer and trotted off down the slope, quite fast as if to make up for lost time.

The scent of early flowering honeysuckle still clung to the slope long after the careless padding footsteps had faded along the well-worn path and an elephant hawk moth probed about the blooms, searching out the deep pots of nectar. A bat, drawn to the plant by the promise of tasty pickings, made its first catch off the plant and flew away to a night time perch to eat in comfort. In a distant larch another night insect eater churred – the nightjar. The sounds of darkness were acquiring their usual quiet reassurance and, deep in her sett, the badger sow sensed it. Familiar Dildawn was breathing cold down into her corridors and she shuffled around and finally ambled upwards; but when her black and white head emerged she paused and with great care read the scents.

Behind her, in carefree abandon, was the noise of playful purring, hurried jostling and enthusiasm; she turned, grunting urgent disapproval, and a hush fell. The cubs knew her tone of voice, knew when obedience was necessary, so they waited without a single yikker while the sow moved out onto the well trampled earth about the family home, lifted her nostrils and sniffed for any unusual scent of danger. There was none, so she turned again to her children and gave her approval. They jogged out, scampering, rolling, tumbling down the steep slope. The sow was reassured, heard Ule, discounted his call, and became increasingly relaxed. She talked to each bundle of energy, nuzzled each in turn as the cubs' play brought them close to her.

The night was now full of mock battles, of yikkerings, high pitched and staccato, whenever one cub nipped another. The sow watched as her cubs' play became more and more independent; finally she looked to herself, scratched energetically with her powerful back claws, and began to repeat the grooming process first demonstrated by the boar – but she was interrupted. One cheeky cub climbed right on top of her, she bowled him over and in one continuous movement held him down on his back and pressed her wet nose into his thinly covered underparts to lick and groom him into badger cleanliness. The cub purred, she replied and scratched him into shape.

Down the slope, way below the sett, Ule was perched low. At first sight it seemed strange behaviour, but he had noticed a slight movement on the woodland floor; there was a noisy crawling and a beetle, nearly forty millimetres long, shuffled into view on slender legs. The lesser stag beetle was food to the owl, despite its armour plating, so although his pellet would later contain a good deal of chitinous waste, Ule took the monster of the rotting woodland floor and swallowed.

Kewick was looking deep into the stream. In mid water there was a shoal of minnows at rest, moving with the ripples. They were clear to see for the sky was full of light. The nearly full moon was at its zenith and the Milky Way was also high to the east and directly above the owls, the Plough and Cassiopeia faced each other brightly. However, there was the problem of refraction, something Kewick would not take account of, for she was no fisherwoman, and there was the wetness. As an opportunist she had to weigh up the risks and set them against the advantages. She glided from her perch. The fish shoal disintegrated with a silent explosion of fear – an owl's hunting shadow across the silver surface – but there were no splashes, no talons probing the water's surface; Kewick had carried her claws across the stream to the bracken on the far bank, and laid hold of a scurrying woodmouse.

Ironically, although both adult owls had flown to find their prey, not far from the oak prey was in abundance. While the owl chicks waited in quiet stillness, a group of woodmice chased and fought. The females encouraged it, running away from the males until they lost interest, then turning back to offer encouragement again until they saw that interest had been rekindled; then they were off – stop-it-I-like-it through the dying flowers, in and out of the starlight. The courting was interrupted by the third-born owl chick. He started up his immature 'kuwit' – 'I'm hungry'. Three times he called, and a sister followed suit. The mice heard, hesitated and scurried deep into the bramble bush.

Ule heard the calls clear and well. Both he and Kewick had eaten and the calls which now filled Dildawn were an irritating reminder of duty. Both birds had flown down to Longland's edge. In the meadow the night was warm and busy. The cows had moved back into the open pasture, away from the stream, and slept or shuffled among the buttercups, their breath sweet and eerie with subdued rustling. There were other sounds, too; the muffled scut of rabbits moving out of their burrows in nervous hops. The young were most vulnerable and Ule watched them in the clear moonlight. One small creature hopped away from the main group of browsing animals and moved down into a slight depression, full of lush, damp, green grass – but there was more than grass: in the two patient eyes of the stoat shone the measure of an efficient pounce. A scream followed and all the adult rabbits feeding at the woodland edge ran away with hesitant hops, finding holes and hideaways, aware that the sacrifice of one meant safety for the rest. Kewick saw and heard, knowing that prey in this part of the wood was now timid and warned. Without waiting for calm to return, she flew off to Alder Island, to find success there.

In the grassy hollow the young rabbit wrestled with death. The stoat was at its neck. Tight, strong teeth closed down onto the left side; one long ear was pinned down into pain, the other stood free and erect while the injured animal struggled feebly. The stoat clung in confidence and determination. Waiting on his branch, Ule saw the movement in the grass and heard the one-sided battle degenerate into rustlings. Although his grip was taut the stoat's body seemed relaxed.

The rabbit gave a final, nervous twitch and death's last gasp faded into silence. Sensing this, the stoat relaxed his hold for a moment and stepped back from his prey. The rabbit was up and away, hopping through the clinging stalks in futile, frustrated escape. The angry stoat bounded back, hard, back at the neck to reclaim his meal, and from that moment there was no struggle, no screaming, only certain death.

The stoat dragged the body towards a tree stump where a convenient bramble bush was growing. With much laboured effort the predator hauled his prey into a hiding place, but within seconds two fiery eyes had reappeared and looked round; with cocked ears he listened intently. Ule watched, still and quiet. The stoat neither saw nor heard anything, so he scuffled back into the bush and dragged the rabbit out by the neck, pulling it over the leaf litter and across to the hedge. Ule abandoned patience, called and made to fly off. The stoat heard the hoot and hurried through a gap, but it was too small, the rabbit would not go. It was stuck! From Alder Island Kewick replied to her mate. The stoat was frantic with haste; he heaved and pulled, then he rushed round to the rear of the dead rabbit, pulled it out of the gap, hurried back to the neck and tried again. Finally, with a long last tug, the body crashed through the twigs and thorns, and stoat and rabbit were out into the grass of Longland and safety.

Ule had flown to the cliff above St Stephen's Falls and perched there – a squat silhouette looking for all the world like a rock ready to tumble from the crumbling edge. He stared at the moon hung like a great lantern in the quietly flowing waters, saw a water vole break the perfect shape with its rippling progress across the stream to its hole on the far bank. There the bracken had unfurled and was high with moths and spiders. He waited, but the vole must have entered by an underwater cavern, for he saw no scrambling up the bank, so headfirst he went, plummeting through the fine spray towards the splash pool, until, at the last moment, he glided upwards, banked left and flew down, with hardly a wing flap, direct to Alder Island and Kewick. There he stopped, considered and waited.

Night passed and the wood echoed to the calls of the owl chicks. Back at the old oak they were disturbed by the noise of the old boar badger sliding down the slope above the sett, taking even the sow by surprise. The young owls had all eaten, although from their urgent-sounding calls both Kewick and Ule knew that it had not been enough. They still hunted, despite the fact that the dawn chorus had begun to swell, and even when the songs faded and a robin turned away from aggression to the needs of maintenance work on his plumage, beating his wings, spinning his head, dipping quickly in a small pool near the waterfall's spray, they continued to perch, waiting.

All the day birds were about, but still the owlets waited in expectation of more food. They stood in a row on a stubby oak, a little way away from the now abandoned nest. Their plumage as yet retained much of the barred downy underparts, and although some feathers of adulthood could be discerned, they were still very much chicks. Chicks in more senses than one, for their curiosity was insatiable. The flight call of a turtle dove caught their attention. They bobbed their heads and located the bird, but their stirrings frightened a blackcap which erupted into alarm; they were so conspicuous sitting out in the open in daylight. So, as they had not learned the tawny owl rule – never be seen by the light of the sun – the small birds of the day came to teach them. Mobbing chaffinches joined the blackcap, and mistle thrushes, but the young predators-to-be sat still and glared back boldly. All the commotion frightened a wood pigeon off her nest with great blusterings, and as she bolted she kicked an egg off the frail stick platform; it dropped and broke, dripping down the branches. But at the oak tree, no matter how much the owlets were mobbed, they would not be moved. In fact once the noisy mob had made their point by locating their presence and pointing it out to the whole wood, they moved off, leaving the chicks alone.

Slowly the day reverted to the sounds of mid morning. A nuthatch scurried headfirst down an oak trunk and five owls snoozed silently in hidden places. Ule and Kewick had done their best to satisfy the wants of the three chicks and had finally driven them away from their open perch into a more secluded spot. The day was full of music; on high points throughout Dildawn blackbirds sang lustily, sweetly and long, while spotted flycatchers flew in and out and around collecting insects from the air, snapping at them with sharp clips. The nuthatch turned and ran back up the tree, searching the deep crevices of the bark for insects of a different kind. At the woodland's edge the air was warm and blowing gently through the branches were gauzy veils of gnats. Those delicate moments, heavy with the scent of May, were disturbed by the cautious stealth of a fierce-eyed pheasant parading out of some low bushes, and in the turning of his red-flecked head came the signal for summer.

❦ 9 ❦

A SUMMER DEATH

There had been a great buzz of excitement in the main street of Ston Gurney. The small boys especially were interested. All day they had pointed and thrown discreet stones, even tried climbing the telegraph pole, but to no avail – an adult had always come along just in time to protect the grey squirrel snoozing on the hot metal capping. Earlier in the day an excited dog had chased it there and so it had stayed in the full light of the sun, hunched up, head hidden by its two front paws, only occasionally changing its precarious position. The Cloud Hill buzzards had either not seen it or discounted the creature as prey because it was so close to houses and people. Six o'clock chimed from the chapel dedicated to St Stephen and the squirrel sat low on his haunches and began to groom himself.

The upper air was full of screaming swifts. White-rumped house martins dived and floated around and about the village gardens. Swallows wove in and out of reeds and under the stone arch of Bendal's Bridge. Through the open doors and windows of the cottages tumbled the unmistakable songs of summer: a male blackbird singing impressively from the topmost branch of the tallest apple tree in the orchard, a whitethroat bubbling from the depths of the hazel scrub near the stream and, echoing down Longland, the call of the cuckoo.

With a final brush of his face the squirrel turned, jerked forward, tested his grip on the downward vertical, and spiralled down in a slow, coarse, scratching corkscrew. Once on the gravel of the roadway he scooted noiselessly over the bridge, into Longland, back on the track to Dildawn and the well known. There, across the field, away from the village, the sunlight of that late afternoon was high in the oak tops, and the same light reached low along the hidden rides to the nooks where, wrapped in cool shade, the five owls were hidden on their separate perches.

A pigeon, high against the sinking sun, hurried towards an old wide-branched oak, its breast lit by long, low rays of warm light. The bird slowed, wheeled and clattered down into the spreading limbs, piercing the wall of foliage with ease, searching out a safe perch amongst the green leaves. Nervously the pigeon looked about. Ule was motionless.

The pigeon puffed out its chest and began: 'Coo, coo, cucoo, cu.'

A soothing sound of the late day, but abruptly the song finished: the pigeon had heard something and stopped to listen. Other wood pigeon, warm in the same sunlight, replied.

Kewick stirred but Ule remained still. The mellowness of the soft evening enveloped all the fields and trees of his territory and beyond, even softening the gaunt ruins of Kingwell Hall. Out of those high walls floated the white owl, silent, like a huge white moth, over the sweetness of the evening. It was bedtime for the children of Hallow's Trow, although the day was still light, and at their curtained bedroom windows a whisper of wind carried pollen and seeds. The wind travelled on, over stone cottages and into Dildawn.

On the quarry floor some late-foraging starlings had found an ants' nest and they hopped about with delight, pecking delicately with their beaks, picking up the ants and inserting the small insects between their feathers. Other starlings noticed and jostled to join in. There was a quarrel, an outburst of noisy, boisterous activity, but it was over in a flurry and the birds reverted to the scurrying ants and their own bristling feathers. Not one ant was harmed. Once the tiny insects had squirted their sterilising formic acid amongst their forceful hosts they were returned to the woodland floor.

Kewick moved out from her tight perch and shook her wings. The first bat of evening flitted out into the cooling air and squeaked. A moth also squeaked, trying to confuse the bat with its high-pitched clicks. Hoverflies, less adept at jamming the hunter's frequency, hung stationary over a clump of wild garlic. A lone spotted flycatcher flew down from its watching post of the day for the last time, snapping up a final crop of gnats. Dimpsey had come to Dildawn and the under-growth was busy with scurrying creatures. Ground beetles were eating their way about the leaf litter as they did each night, preying on smaller insects.

Suddenly Ule tensed. He listened carefully. The cat was back, padding almost silently through the evening shadows. Kewick moved back towards the trunk, and lengthened her shape. But it was not owls that the cat had spotted, it was a weasel dragging a large brown rat to her hidden home under the old moss-covered wall. The cat's eyes had been drawn to the movement, slow and laboured. It was certainly a rich prize, two for the price of one pounce. The tom cat crouched still and waited for the weasel with taut muscles. Although the weasel was cautious, she was unconscious of the cat's watching presence. Nearer and nearer she came, and then suddenly the cat sprang.

The noise slightly startled the owls but they remained silent. The monster came at the weasel through the low dark air in speed and surprise, but even so, the attacked was prepared for the assassin. She dropped the rat and met the cat coming down, fastening her teeth onto an outstretched paw. The cat screamed in pain and rage, shook his paw frantically and turned his head to bite, and again with keen instinct the weasel reacted, letting go only to bite once more, this time deep into the tom cat's face where she hung on. The cat bounded away from the rat, scrabbling at the pain imploding in his head, but the weasel would not let go. Across the quarry floor ran the cat, shaking, spitting, and as suddenly as she had bitten, the weasel released her grip and fell back to the ground, leaving the cat to continue his ignominious retreat. For one brief moment the weasel stood chittering in triumph, but in an instant she was scurrying back to the rat and the effort of dragging her prey to a safe, undisturbed place. Normality returned. The dusk chorus tailed away as the birds left off their song in turn: first wren, then chaffinch, blackcap and blackbird and finally robin, as always outsinging even wood pigeon, cuckoo and song thrush.

Kewick moved out again along the branch, and Ule also stirred. In the pipistrelle colony there was much activity. They were all females there and, earlier in the day, one had hung head upwards, made a pouch by bending forward her tail and given birth into it. Now that same mother eased herself out from between the ivy leaves to feed, with a new life clinging tightly to the pumping strength of her breast. Into Dildawn they flew together, mother and baby, surrounded by brushing sounds and buffeting warmth.

Another insect eater of the night crouched low along the length of a beech branch.

'Kirrrrrrrrrrrr-oo-kirrrrrrrrrrrrr-oo-kirrrrrrrrrrrrrr,' churring and rising, churring and falling; the song of the nightjar. Distant came the reply, the flight call of the male: 'Crooo-eek.' And as his wings beat rapidly the familiar whip crack echoed through the trees.

Chestnuts bulked large in the glimmering light. The stars shone out quietly luminous and dark came swiftly. A slight wind blew on, faintly rustling the bushes, carrying with it the mysterious sound of night, out of the pure black shadows the melancholic: 'Hoo, horoo!'

The song floated over the darkling wood and the owl chicks heard it. There was little noise from them, but the third-born let out a tentative, begging, 'Kuwit'. He was hungry. The parents were quiet, too, and less eager to respond to the demands of their chicks. The owlets were able to fly now; their feathers were almost adult and the two sisters had already learnt to hunt. They had successfully captured prey for themselves. Ule flew to within sight of the male chick, watched him, heard his screeching call. He called gently then flew away. Kewick had already flown, up to St Stephen's Falls. The two sisters followed her, without their mother's encouragement. All the owls were moulting, the chicks losing their hold on immaturity and the adult birds replacing the worn feathers of a year's hard work.

Close, but not together, the owl family enjoyed the spray and the shallow pools. The third-born chick still sat at a distance and called repeatedly: 'Kwirick, kuwick, kuwit!' Ule was not at the falls either, but he ignored the young male owl, and finally moved away to hunt for himself. Up at the waterfall the last curling feathers of down floated on dark pools; the two female owlets and Kewick had abandoned their preening and also flown to hunt. The male owlet called again, but there was no reply and no owl came close to him. The Milky Way was a silver brush stroke across the sky, swirling wide at the southern horizon, and Hercules stood proud, high in the south; the night was open and the third-born male flew off, on his own, to hunt. Like his father before him he flew northwards and came close to Friggle Street, for he did not know of the danger of cars. Here he rested, waiting, on a tree close to Greyfield's outbuildings.

The invasion of rats which had occurred unnoticed some weeks before, had become a worry to the woman at the house. Although she was sympathetic to wild creatures, her fear of the fecundity of rats had caused her to contact the local pest man. He had come with his blue-stained grain and carefully laid it in safe hiding places – safe, that is, except to rats and their young, and there were plenty of young. Having moved, the rats had set about breeding and there were many young rats, unknowing and careless, about all Greyfield's paths and buildings, young rats eating poison because it was freely available.

So fortune and fate brought the young owl to Greyfield and he waited in a tree.

'Kirrrrrrrrrrrrrrr-oo-kirrrrrrrrrrrrr-oo-kirrrrrrrrrrrrr,' the nightjar again broke into the quietness of the night. It was the time for the open beak and the hunting ploy. The young owl sensed it and concentrated hard.

Straying from the gravel of Greyfield's yard, twitching and rustling on the woodland floor, came a young rat. She tottered, hesitated, her curious path described several circles. She was conspicuous – the movement, the noise, the slow progress – and the owl had learnt well; he glided down and with capable talons swooped his prey away into the dark night of his woodland perch. It was his first unaided, unsupervised kill, and it was perfectly timed and neatly executed. He flew away from Greyfield and chose an eating place closer to his familiar trees. The young rat was no larger than a woodmouse; he crushed the skull and swallowed it whole. Distant came the call of one of his sisters. He heard it but did not respond.

Twice more that night the owl flew back to the same tree close to Greyfield, and twice more that night he took a young rat whose stomach was filled with warfarin. Tragically, like other birds of prey, he was, accidentally and unknowingly, taking poison.

*   *   *

Dildawn was full of incident that night. The darkness was white with flitting shadows: moths interpreting the delicate variety of Dildawn's night time scents. The minute scurryings of insects of all sizes through and over the ground litter were deafened by the strident calls of the bush cricket. Nothing seemed still, even the sow badger seemed to bustle with more haste than usual, but she was chasing a promising scent. Carefully she followed it and it led her, as she had supposed, to the breeding stop of a young doe rabbit. The small chamber was somewhat distant from the burrow because the young female was the least dominant in the warren. Sadly she had not long resealed the hole after feeding her small family and had left the tiny rabbits to the mercy of the night. That night had no mercy! With powerful claws designed for heavy digging, the badger scratched her way towards the litter and much-needed sustenance.

At the side of the badger, within a paw's reach, a young woodmouse was out feeding, too. It twitched, listened, smelt and moved forward in nervous hops, then almost bumped into a long, fat, juicy black slug, such was its shortsightedness. The mouse advanced, the slug's horns withdrew, and the creature began to contract into itself. Whiskers and teeth chattered about the black rubbery skin. It was very sticky and the mouse was puzzled; it hopped back and wiped its whiskers, hesitated, then hopped forward again to take another lick. The slug was still sticky. The small mouth and nose wrinkled and tried to winkle a way around the slime, but there was no way, and because the mouse was neither desperate nor adventurous it turned away and washed its face with an urgent thoroughness before scrurrying off to search the woodland floor for less messy food.

And there were stranger happenings in Dildawn's short night. A great, rustling shape moved across and down the slope, enveloping twenty square inches of woodland floor as it went. A small, white polythene bag. The second-born sister saw it first. It was an unknown colour and shape but it moved erratically and it could have been prey hanging over the dying stalks of bluebells; in its movement it took on a three-dimensional shape. So the young owl launched out to practise her newly acquired hunting skills. She struck hard and keen but there was nothing to grasp. Her sharp talons cut right through the bag and as she flapped upwards, although her claws were empty, around her fluffy thighs there was a noisy flapping. She twisted and turned and kicked out, but she could not loosen the hold of the bag tangled round her leg. The unfamiliar flapping sounds frightened her and her erratic flight path made the noise more menacing as it seemed to follow her. When she glided in to land she tumbled, for her talons were blunted by the polythene which flapped forward and upset the precision of her landing. She circled again, swooped down to the ground and there, with furious tearing, attacked the source of her fright with indiscriminate blows of her beak and sharp talons; after much effort and noise she ripped herself free and flew away, back to her perch, another lesson well learnt.

All night the swifts flew high, racing the dark clouds which scudded unseen above the valley. They were so high that not even Ule heard them, but as the sky brightened over the distant fields beyond Starvelark, their jet-black wings zoomed down the narrowing tunnel of night into the liquid gold of another summer dawn. At Dildawn's western edge, in the fields beyond Longland, the owl family had come together in a desultory sort of way. First Kewick came to rest in the morning light, eyes closed against the brightness, then Ule. The two sisters saw their parents enjoying the gentleness of early warmth on drying bales of hay and copied them. Finally the male owlet came, at a distance, and spread his wings too. Although they were creatures of the night they still had a need for health-giving sunrays. So five pairs of wings were spread out across the sweet-smelling bundles, and the full, intricate beauty of the tawny owl's feather pattern was revealed, the translucent strength of the delicate tail fan.

For a quarter of an hour they lay in the full sun, exposing each feather directly and throwing their heads right back to reveal an almost scraggy neck. Then Kewick stirred. She stood up, shook her wings and preened herself, pecking off a few lingering blades of dry hay. The chicks followed her example, but Ule remained still, enjoying extra moments of warmth. He stirred when he heard his mate fly off. She took the lead, followed closely by her offspring, although each bird flew its separate way. Kewick, with a panting throat and warmed wings, flew straight to her daytime roost; the female owlets roosted quite close by in two separate oaks; the male chick was hesitant and alighted on two trees before finally choosing a branch close by his mother, overlooking her. Meanwhile Ule cleaned himself down and took a long leisurely flight along a field boundary, creating mayhem amongst small birds as his shadow fell over their nests holding young second broods.

The whole of Dildawn was watchful during that leafy summer day. Although the bats were back in the cracks and crevices of the quarry, hidden well from the vagaries of the day, the old stone wall bustled with noisy rustlings. A slim, neat-bibbed weasel snaked out of the goose grass and campion and stood upright on her hind legs. Almost taut with tense alertness, she looked all round, then disappeared back into her crack in the wall. In just as long as it took a wren to rattle out its five-second warble she was back, her mouth full of life. Again she looked about her with great care, then she began to slink and glide away. The dawn chorus had almost faded but the creature travelled so lightly that her departure made no sound, only the noisy clatter of a wood pigeon taking off and climbing steeply, clapping its wings all the time; up and down it went, over the humps of its flight, across Longland and into the distant arm of Dildawn. Quietness fell again, but for the lazy, soporific 'poooooorr-poooooorr' of a turtle dove and the imperceptible rustle of the weasel returning, sliding through the campion and goose grass back to her crack in the wall. She re-emerged, looking round very carefully; her mouth was full again and off she snaked through the undergrowth; she had decided to move house, and was carrying her young in her mouth, one by one, to the new hole in deeper, more secluded haunts.

On St Stephen's wet rocks stood a water ouzel, resting, waiting to walk the stream bed in search of its food. The owls neither saw nor heard it as it flew suddenly down from the rocks on its short whirring wings. Quick and white breasted, with unmistakable speed it flew to its wading spot, ignoring the bassooning dragonflies which hawked in and out of the purple loosestrife and over the yellow flags. The dipper's hunting was hidden; walking underwater up the bed of the stream, the fast-flowing water pressing down on its broad back and keeping it on its feet. Above the singing waters was a metallic blue pounce, a sudden sally of hairy legs dark in the sunshine, down on to a grey fly. Because the attack of the dragonfly came out of the summer sky, without warning, the fly was helpless and was carried away easily to a dry, warm stone. There the feast was prepared: wings were ripped off and fluttered gently into the flowing stream. The dipper was back on its rocky perch flexing its legs, blinking its white eyelids, its sweet song warbling clearly above the noise of the tumbling waters.

Distant and deep in the heart of an oak, the brittle wings of sunlight stirred and the young owl could not sleep. Discomfort filled his daytime perch. The slow hours were made longer by unease and filled with the chattering of yellowhammers which had bustled down the long green tongue of Longland from the more open fields of the north-west. 'Chiz-iz-iz-iz-iz-iz-iz-zeee', in and out of the hedgerow, all along the woodland edge, the small birds travelled. To have roosted so far west, right at the

edge of Dildawn, was unusual for Ule and Kewick, but as parents they were anxious to extend their chicks' knowledge of territory and hunting terrain. The young owls had to learn to hunt away from their parents' territory, on their own and without help.

The young owl stirred fitfully. Flies of all sorts were vibrating in the sunlight; females were quivering, lying back for a micro-second's attention from the male. Blackbirds and tits had built the second nest of summer and begun another noisy round of territorial defence. On the woodland floor the ground heaved noisily with the efforts of scavenging beetles.

The male owlet heard it all and was easily disturbed. Yet, despite the long uncomfortable days, he hunted on through warm July, finding in the easy haunts of Greyfield a satisfaction for his hunger. He did not, could not associate the pain deep inside him with his poisoned prey, and despite discomfort and encouragement from his parents to extend his range, each night he returned to those poisoned hunting grounds. For several more nights he hunted, easily and well; for several more nights he fed eagerly, and the warfarin which accumulates over a short period did its work. If only he had varied his hunting, chosen different types of prey, varied the place of his killing, but he did not, and late in the dying darkness of a new dawn's chorus he failed to respond to the roosting call of Ule; the lastborn chick did not return to roost near the family group. That was part of the plan – departure from his father's land – but it was premature, although, from Ule's point of view, not untimely: better early than late! So neither Ule nor Kewick, nor even his sisters, searched out the third and last born. Had they looked they would have found him. His last despairing flight had taken him back to the old oak, that familiar tree right at Dildawn's heart. There, at the foot of the age-scarred monster, the young male owl crashed down and died, on his back.

*　　*　　*

The evening after his death was windless and very warm. Solemn pink spires of rosebay willow herb grew skywards from the roadside verge and, through those stalks, a tentative black tongue flickered at intervals. The slender body of the slow worm made its way over a rusting shaft cable and glided with grace towards a fern-hung bank, all that remained of the Earl of Warwick's coalmine and the tramway that used to carry off the 'black diamonds' of the nineteenth century. The creature moved precisely over the wreckage of man's dreams; its rich copper-coated body, warm and shining, flowed in silent perfection and two tiny black eyes looked urgently about. The echoes of fifty years of hacking picks and straining ponies, of winding gear and swirling flood waters, had long since faded, eighty years ago and more, but in the solidly built mine offices a human still fidgeted and fretted. Although the woman from Greyfield did not intrude into the lives of the owls, she was watchful of them and knew them well, and so it was she who found and recognised the disaster for which she, in part, was responsible – the death of the young owl.

Earlier in the day she had walked into the heart of Dildawn, looking for signs of the owl family, and near the nest hole she saw the body, picked it up and took it home, to Greyfield. For most of the day she thought about the bird lying in the outhouse and she began the task of searching out all the poison. When she had collected all that she could find she put it and the dead body on the garden bonfire and with a deep sigh she set light to the pyre of clippings, warfarin and owl. Rats were a problem, yet she resolved, silently but firmly, that she would never again resort to poison; traps perhaps, but never poison. It was, she knew, reasonably safe to use warfarin, for it was not long lasting and for a bird the size of an owl to acquire warfarin indirectly was unusual, an accident. Nevertheless it had happened, and she had been the cause.

The smoke rose straight into the air, billowing coarsely into the clear sky. Disturbed by the activity in Greyfield and by the strange smells, the legless lizard moved off and away, leaving the woman tending the bonfire and looking idly at the webs of courting spiders – the female sitting in the centre of her fragile domain and males approaching carefully to play tantalising tunes of vibrating love.

As the snapping cracklings of the fire broke down into the disintegrating glowing heart, she turned and walked into the paddock behind the house. The air was full of the continuous droning of grasshoppers, a sure sign that shrews, though secretive and well hidden, were eating well. High summer scents filled the twilight air. Hoverflies hung above flowering marjoram and on the rounded flowerhead a burnet moth pushed and shoved about, eager to dip its tongue into the nectar; safe in the instinctive knowledge that only an inexperienced insect-eating bird would pick it off for food, not recognising the red and black for what it was: a warning against a bitter taste. All around the hedgerow blackflies circled, buzzing through the stillness of the evening, and into that quiet fullness came, loud and clear, the last song of the blackcap. The woman paused, listened and, after lingering with an enjoyment tinged with sadness, she went indoors.

Also on the northern edge of Dildawn, at the roadway's boundary, two young tawny owls lingered. The two immature females were extending their explorations to the scents of the road. Even at a height of twelve feet, on a convenient perch in a dying elm, the smell of warm tar was plain, rising on the evening air. The road below them was black, smooth and straight between its banks. The verge at the side of Friggle Street was an easy hunting ground. The road itself was a barrier, making the wild woodland edge an animal highway. The birds waited and watched as a small, young rabbit hopped cautiously down the bank, but as it reached the harsh surface of Friggle Street a loud noise came from beyond the bend in the road. In an instant white light filled their world with fear. It flashed red and black. The owls sat motionless, but the rabbit lay sideways on the road, twitching, trying to crawl to its feet: a large prey, made easy by the collision.

Silently in the moonrise, one owl took the creature, lifted the victim to her perch. Owls do not eat carrion, kills have to be fresh, but opportunism is all part of being a successful hunter, her parents had taught her that. However, as she carried the awkward victim, it slipped from her clasp, toppled over the branch and onto the woodland floor. The other owl was there first, pecking and clawing. There was a squabble between the two sisters, more noise in the darkness. It disturbed a hedgehog deep in the damp undergrowth, munching on a living frog, but a pair of short-tailed field voles were so wrapped up in their own quarrel that they did not hear the owls at all.

*   *   *

The last of the summer months came to lie heavily on the land. Brambles and wild roses shed their petals. Campion was over and while scabious flowered, the young, newborn creatures of the year rushed about, searching for a key to survival during the coming winter. The autumn brimstones emerged from their chrysalids, fluttering about in their preparations for hibernation, many to choose the ivy for their resting place because their resemblance to the underside of an ivy leaf was uncanny. The cuckoos were silent as they prepared for their journey back to Africa, but Ule also prepared, and in his preparation he had to find his voice. As the month deepened he began to hoot. It was not loud or persistent, but it was an indication to his daughters that they should leave Dildawn, should find new territories for themselves, away from him; and not long after sundown, Kewick called too, in agreement with her mate.

10

AUTUMN RENEWAL

Tall rods of rosebay willow herb, topped with silver balls of thistledown, glinted in the golden twilight, and red leaves of beech and hornbeam dropped silently. A robin sang lustily from the yellowing hazel. It was autumn. A slow worm moved towards an unsuspecting slug – a smooth motion through the grass. He seized the slug from above and across the middle. There was a writhing struggle and a curling, desperate extrusion of slime, but although the slow worm's face was almost covered in thick mucus, the creature continued with its evening meal. The robin sang on, and distant but clear came Ule's territorial affirmation; day and night overlapped. The lizard's meal was over, but before moving off he deliberately wiped his face on the ground, brushing it roughly against the grass, and some of the excess slime was removed before the creature slid on into dense, cool cover.

A golden light flooded Longland's rich pasture and, as a few tattered butterflies flitted into distant haze, there was a strange and sudden chill of wind. The splintered grass was bound with the glittering snares of hopeful spiders, and above the grass a myriad insects were hatching, climbing and flying. Five bats were hushed and busy in a fragile flight, swooping down to the grass tops, tasting well the profusion. Fruit was falling in the valley, tumbling down the slopes; every bush, every stem seemed bent and weighed down with food. Berries, especially elder and blackberry, provided a magnificent feast for all the local animals. The grass below and around the bramble bush was laced with a network of

runs. Each day and every night, beaks and teeth pecked and munched through the oozing sweetness.

The young owls were meat eaters, so blackberries were of no direct interest to them, but the first-born owlet had learnt from Ule and Kewick that bramble bushes were a good place to wait for prey. In that September twilight she flew to her own bush, right at Dildawn's eastern edge, overlooking the distant cottages of Hallow's Trow. She flew in silently, although a flock of roosting starlings noticed her shadow and were stirred into noisy waves of agitation. They bustled up dark and guttural, but the owl ignored them and chose her perch carefully. Slowly the starlings settled back into silent sleep.

The moon was new and rose early into the clear darkness. High above the owl, hidden by the russets of Dildawn's dying leaves, the Milky Way stretched right across the sky from west to east, and sinking before it, dominating the southern sky, Pegasus rode silently. The owls were not together, not even near to each other, for although sometimes the young females had been allowed to haunt hunting grounds almost in company with their parents, Ule was becoming increasingly intolerant of his progeny. He wanted to rid his woods of them. So while one sister waited near the bramble, the second-born was up at Friggle Street, close to the road's edge. The parents themselves were on the other side of Longland, staring out at the fields of Ston Gurney. They, too, were some distance apart, for although Ule tolerated his mate and she his presence, the owl family had broken up.

Clouds forced shadows to move across the copper-coated slopes, and in that flecked darkness the first-born owl waited for woodmice to come and eat the fruit of the bramble. It was a dusty darkness; the wind blew, trees groaned and scraped; one cracked and a small branch broke off, making the starlings chatter again. The owl ignored their babble. Cloud cover became complete and it was so dark that even the owl's eyes found little to concentrate and distil into meaning. So the young bird relied on her hearing, and despite the rustling wind whispering hoarsely through the branches, she heard another sound, a different sound, pricking across the litter of the woodland floor. A small animal stalked the scented darkness, its whiskers twitching and tasting the air. It had strayed from its usual haunts and was hurrying through the gathering gloom, equally intent on finding victims amongst the rotting fruit.

The weasel was alert and busy and the young owl pinpointed its sound. She launched out and down but it was no simple capture, for the weasel snapped and struggled. Needle-like teeth sank deeply into the sinews of the owl's upper leg. She flapped away with her prey but she was confused; for a moment she hesitated and her talons clasped more firmly, but the teeth brought more pain to her thigh and she felt it keenly. Frightened by the unexpected, the unusual, she slackened her grip and let the weasel go. For a moment the small red-brown mammal hung in the air by the strength of its own teeth, then as suddenly as it was taken it fell to the ground, leaving the injured owl to fly back to a silent and painful perch, fortunate to have escaped.

So, too, the weasel. In an instinctive reflex, as it fell it twisted and landed on its feet, squirmed for a moment then scurried away into the safety of the bramble. It had been badly mauled by the sharp claws and, although well hidden from the night, it was much weakened by wounds and shock. Whether its resting place would be a place of recovery, somewhere to lick wounds and recoup courage, or a bed of death, only time would tell.

The young owl on her branch was dishevelled, shaking and nervous, her mind a tumble of instincts and reflexes. Below her a hedgehog unballed after the fright of hearing the weasel spit and fight. He had been feeding on fallen crab apples and a few of these, impaled on his spiny edge, still clung to his back as he moved forwards to sniff at a particular leaf. He began to lick the leaf enthusiastically, becoming noisier as his tongue moved more and more rapidly. The young owl trembled and began to preen in an attempt to distract her thoughts from the fright and the pain. The sky cleared of cloud and she saw the strange antics of the hedgehog quite clearly. A foamy saliva had accumulated in his mouth and white bubbles began to exude from the sharp brown snout. The hedgehog reared up on his front legs and turned his body onto one side, throwing his spiny back into small, regular corrugations. Fleas on the skin rushed about and, with the soft underparts exposed, the old boar began to throw his head round and round, spreading saliva froth all about his flanks. The crab apples slid off his spines in the vigour of self-anointing, but the creature seemed neither to notice nor care. The owl continued to watch carefully, for there was so much noise in the astonishing outburst that the hedgehog demanded attention.

And as the owl waited, watched and rested, so began the slow process of recovery. For long minutes she sat in silent stillness; she heard Ule call, not to her, but to the whole wood: his call of possession. His message to her was clear: 'Keep out! This wood is mine!' And all the while the hedgehog was busy, oblivious of all sounds and sensations save his sticky, licking, slobberings. Above him the slightest wisp of sound went by – a quiet shadow – unnoticed. It was the owl testing the night ways again, making a tentative flight to an old and dying elm high above the twinkling beads of amber – night-lit Hallow's Trow main road. The fright that the weasel had given her had triggered off an instinctive response, a decision not to hunt near that bramble bush again, and because the heart of Dildawn and the flat pasture of Longland belonged to her father, there was no choice – she blinked eastwards – she had to flap across the flashing road, fly over the guttering, snuffing lights of the village, on across the dark fields of another hillside and up to Starvelark Wood. She had seen it often enough from Dildawn's eastern edge and she saw it again, a smudge on her dark horizon. Starvelark was quiet, she could not hear its voices, but Dildawn was full of her father: the wind brought his voice clearly across the valley, through the trees, and there was another sound, quite close to her as she stood purposefully on shaky legs and hesitated.

It was the old male badger. She waited to hear what he was about. He snuffled and sniffed under the dry litter, searching out worms and anything else. That night he was in luck. With a quick flip of his powerful claws he opened up a wasps' nest. The coolness of the night had made the insects lethargic and he grubbed down with his snout, digging and turning over, trying to search out the juicy young grubs, tender morsels, a special delight. Now and again he raised his head and shook it to get rid of the wasps which crawled all about his face, but they did not seem to trouble him, and as wasps' nests are full of more and more grubs right up to the first penetrating frost, he was not easily distracted from a favourite meal.

The owl waited until the badger had finished his meal and waddled off. A quietness returned; only the occasional thump of a falling chestnut intervened. The first-born owl called, quietly at first, and it was not the immature begging call of childhood. She became bolder and called more loudly; Ule heard her and challenged her with his own cry, so she glided out over the meadow and flew on her way to her new territory on the hill near ruined Kingwell Hall – to Starvelark Wood.

*   *   *

By coincidence, as his daughter left Dildawn Ule returned to the old oak, the site of the female owl's birth. It was a temporary perch, a song post, a place from which to call out his territorial rights, again and again. He was early in turning his thoughts to the coming year, for there were creatures on that same tree which had yet to live out their cycle for the present year. A female vapourer moth rested from the effort of her emergence. She had only recently climbed out of her cocoon and she waited close by the abandoned case. Although her day-flying mate was a normally shaped moth with drab brown wings, she was a tubby barrel of an insect, more like a woodlouse than a fluttering beauty. All she possessed in the form of wings were tiny vestigial stumps, so even in the daytime she did not travel far; indeed, if a mate found her, more than likely she would lay her eggs all over her cocoon case.

Ule had no time to spend looking for a moth, he was much more interested in his own mate. Kewick had heard him call and she returned to the centre of the wood to join him. She watched Ule from a distance, on a different, separate tree. Neither of the adult birds knew that one of their daughters had flown away. Just like the death of the young male, earlier in the year, they would notice by omission, notice that Dildawn seemed a little emptier. So Ule sat, waited, watched, called and then listened, and if only Kewick's voice echoed back he would know that Dildawn was his again, and only his.

So the season progressed. The earth rolled on round the sun, and Dildawn was tilted farther away from its warm rays. But the days were still mild and full of life. Blue tits still searched the oak tree's bark for insects and spiders. Jays and squirrels quarrelled over acorns, and another, much smaller creature, the acorn weevil, no larger than an apple pip, moved across the tree infesting as she went, drilling holes in each oak seed, laying eggs, sealing the holes and leaving her young to hatch out into larvae. At night, when the wind came biting cold from the east and north it brought with it more than cold chill, it carried the voice of the first-born female owl, distant but clear, and Ule responded. His calls not only reassured his daughter of his continuing presence but served to keep her out of his wood.

Such noisy threats seemed to mean very little to the second female, however. Now fully mature, she still haunted Dildawn, taking care to stay well clear of her father, although that was not so easy. Like the common wasp she had become a nuisance, hanging on to the sweet fruit of Dildawn and Longland despite her father's intolerance of her presence. Kewick too, when the owl chick's hunting area overlapped with her own, showed threat to her own daughter. So as the leaves' fall became a blizzard and the long evenings pushed back man's clock, the young female owl began to live dangerously. Yet she would not loose her hold on Dildawn.

*   *   *

119

It was well into October, the moon's last quarter. Cygnus and Andromeda were high and bright in the early evening when Ule and Kewick began to call to each other. The female chick was still in Dildawn and she was silent; she had no reason to make her presence known, indeed she needed to hide herself, which was why she had chosen to haunt an area her father never visited – the roadside verge at the side of Friggle Street. She was quite close to Greyfield and she was causing especial interest to the woman of the house because she was clinging so tightly to the edge of her parents' territory. The woman had talked at length to her husband about the second female and had been going out into the evening for several nights to listen and watch for signs of the young owl. The bird's behaviour was worthy of note.

True to her recent form, the young owl was perched again at the side of Friggle Street, wary, ears strained and sinews tensed. A bank vole scurried out into the cool night, down onto the tarmac. The female owl swooped. Distant in the heart of Dildawn Ule called. She heard her father and there was a fumbling. Into the darkness drove the same bright light that had terrified him years before. Feathers blew in the whack of wind, there was a sideways impact – first the aerial, then the windscreen's corner pillar. Limply the owl slid over the roof and into the wake of the disappearing car. The second-born owl lay there, quivering, victim of her own mistake.

She heard her mother's reply to Ule, fading, distant, but she did not call; instead she listened to the waterfall's murmurings, and high above her, almost where the stars pricked holes in the blackness, in those distant skyways of the night, she heard the summer migrants flying by. Soon into those same starlit roads from the byways of the north would come other travellers, from a cooler summer: redwings and fieldfares. The owl should have heard their return too, but all she heard was the wind scudding along the tarmac and another sound, low, close to the ground, echoing along the flat expanse of barren stone and coming closer: footsteps.

She heard that well and her eyes caught flashes of another light bearing down on her, coming out of the darkness of the road. It was a smaller light than the first, but more searching – a torchlight whose beam swept the roadway. The woman at Greyfield had come out to find her. She knew that it was illegal to take an owl from the wild, for they are a protected species, but she was licensed to look after birds of prey and so she bent quietly and carefully over the injured bird and hooded it with a large handkerchief. It was a precaution more associated with falconry, but she did it to keep shock in the creature to a minimum.

Then she lifted the young owl gently into a deep, warm box – a shelter from the night wind – and at the bottom of the box was a small quantity of straw. The box was closed and the owl sensed movement as the container was carried very carefully back along the road towards the outhouses at Greyfield. Unknowingly the bird was disorientated.

For long moments the owl heard little, felt less and saw nothing. There was a dull ache in her wing and a terrible shaking, an uncontrollable quivering. She lay still, as still as at her daytime perch, but the trembling continued. Suddenly, outside, the movement stopped and the owl no longer felt suspended, for there was now a firmness about her world again. Above her head she heard slow, soft rustles, followed by other sounds: gentle, almost tremulous; not Kewick, not owl, not any kind of bird, not even prey; a soft voice, reassuring, but a sound not of the owl's own night. The bird lengthened her shape, felt the pain in her right wing, shuffled close to the box corner, sensed a strange smell and drowsed into sleep.

It was the right wing which had been broken by the car aerial. A very gentle hand moved delicately across the feathers, found and identified the break and knowledgeably folded the wing back into rest against the body. The woman checked that the bones were in good apposition and well supported by the body wall, then she began the difficult process of fixing sticky tape. She was uncertain, because although her method had worked well with smaller birds, the owl seemed a much more daunting prospect. There was hesitation in her mind, although her hands deftly cut and measured the lengths of tape required. She had heard that plaster applied to a bandage and wrapped round could be used, but she had confidence in the tape method, and decided to risk the danger of it slipping.

Carefully she took the owl in her hands and laid a strip of sticky tape face upwards along the bird's back, from the skull to just beyond the tips of the flight feathers, then she applied another piece to encircle the owl's body, including both wings on a level just behind the wing butt. It was delicate, precise work and she sighed with the effort. She took a third piece and, like the second, applied it sticky side down but encircling the body lower down around the flight feather tips and the tail. Finally she doubled back the longitudinal strip in an attempt to stop the chest band slipping down. It was done well and she considered it carefully, checked the sticky joints, made sure they were well seated; but she had another thought: all the additional weight might unbalance the owl, so she added a counter-balancing strip of tape at the back of the lower band. She sighed again, hoped it would do, and placed the

121

injured creature back in the box, closing the lid quietly but firmly. Then she stepped back and left the outhouse for her kitchen and a cup of tea.

The night passed, but there was nothing to tell the wakening owl that dawn was breaking. Sounds were muffled, the sunlight was hidden and she was insulated from the real world. Several times during the day she tried to shuffle about, but there was no flying, so she rested and blinked her eyes from time to time, for the hood had gone. But despite concentrating hard there was no depth, no width to the darkness; although there was a beyond, for the muffled sounds told her that. Slowly, through the long hours of isolation, these sounds began to develop a meaning. The hidden, unknown world did possess some familiarity: gravel crunched, brakes squealed, engines started and dogs barked. Outside a robin sang fiercely and late-flying wasps and hover-flies buzzed in, out and about the broken window panes of the stone shed. Sounds but no sights, and always there was the weight that tugged at her wings, the tightness about her chest.

Late in the day footsteps approached; the squeaking door opened and after a few moments the box lid was rustled open. Full brown eyes glared upwards. The bird shuffled awkwardly into a corner away from the poking tweezers which held raw beef wrapped in feathers. She refused the food. There was little unnecessary movement; the young owl had to eat and the woman made sure that she did, then retreated into the gathering darkness. As she walked back towards her kitchen door she heard Ule. She stopped to listen. Kewick replied. They were calling out their rights to Dildawn. Both their daughters had left the wood, and their son too; they were preparing for another spring. From the stone-built shed came a tentative, tremulous hoot. The woman smiled weakly, opened the back door and a shaft of light reached up into the purple sky; she closed the door firmly behind her. Ule called down Longland's way, Kewick replied, but no one up as far as Greyfield heard her. Night deepened, the occupants of Greyfield went to bed and silence reigned in the stone outbuilding, but the young owl heard her father from time to time, and in her box she shuffled awkwardly.

*   *   *

Long days passed. Nights were empty, dark and quiet. Twice each day there was a rustling at the box lid and food – dead chicks from the local battery farm – was handed over. So the second-born owl chick rested and recovered, the trembling stopped, the ache faded and only the weight and tightness round her chest remained. To relieve the monotony she bill-clicked, made attempts at preening and shuffled. She became used to the gentle hands lifting her, checking the tape, looking closely at her plumage, placing her on a perch to let her look out at the dimness of the shed.

Since the frightening light, the sharp blow and the pain, life had changed beyond recognition, but the owlet had begun to map out the limited range of her new, confined world. She was in Dildawn still, she knew that from its distant muffled voices, but she also knew that she was not *of* the wood. And there were other changes too. Around her left leg, just above the talons, was a strap; this fastened her loosely to a perch when the woman brought her out of the box, but for most of her day and all of her night it was the warm, closed box that she knew.

Another dusk came. The owl knew, not from the falling light intensity, but from the chorus of birds around Greyfield. The shed door opened and, after feeding, the woman took the owl out of the box and attached her to the perch; then carefully and gently she removed the tape and examined the wing. The owl shook open its wings. There was stiff familiarity in its movement. The woman spoke softly and the owl, which had flapped off the perch and scrambled about on the floor of the shed, allowed itself to be picked up and returned to the perch. There, once again, she wing-stretched and called, gently. The woman smiled. The owl felt with her beak, preened. There was freedom and a difficult but sure balance. Gently the woman returned the owl to the box, closed it firmly and left. Wing-flapping inside the box was difficult and so the owl remained still.

As more days passed the owl was lifted out of her box, tethered to her perch and allowed to flap her wings, to test them. And when the woman felt the wing and saw the strength, she decided to feed the owl for the last time. The young owl took the chick whole, downed it and then bill-clicked loudly as the woman took hold of her and placed her back in the box. The lid closed above her and again there was the sense of movement. Although she was totally enclosed, sounds seemed clearer. Distant in the early night came the melancholy cry of a male tawny owl. Ule! She recognised her father, he was close to Greyfield, and from deep inside her box she replied. She was well and strong and she called. Ule heard and was puzzled; he called again strongly, but the box had been placed carefully in the back of the van, strapped down, and the doors slammed shut. So, leaving Ule calling clearly, the woman drove off, away from Dildawn.

It was no pet in her box, the woman had made sure of that; loved, but not caressed by her hand. All the while she had planned efficiently for these minutes, had chosen her destination with care. The van followed the road round the wood. It was not the straight route of a hunting owl's flight, but along Friggle Street onto the main road, through Hallow's Trow and then back onto a country lane. She was driving deliberately away from the busy routes and the dangers of cars. The small van bumped along a track, up the contours, out onto Kiteley Hill where there were trees and fields. The woman of Greyfield knew them well. She also knew that they were fields unclaimed by other tawny owls. The van was parked in the open darkness, the box retrieved and opened. The strap on the owl's leg was removed. There was a moment's hesitation before the second-born stretched open her wide wings and climbed into the night sky.

*   *   *

In Dildawn, as at Kiteley, the night was light. A full moon had begun to climb slowly above the trees, and because it was still quite low it was easy to see the Milky Way swirling high across the darkness from east to west; at its apex the twinkling 'W' of Cassiopeia glittered. Everywhere the stars' clarity was piercing, even Orion's Belt low on the eastern horizon shone out clear. Ule, flying to his hunting perch, was the only dark shadow. Above him he heard a sound of the season, a different sound, for things were changing, preparing for the coming winter. It came clear, that thin, hissing 'Seeeip', and again, 'Seeeip', high and distant: redwings in flight, passing overhead. Some would drop down from the star-filled pathway and come to share Dildawn during the cold hard months, but the passage of the redwings above him evoked a strong response. He alighted and called and Kewick replied. The call of his second-born daughter, earlier in the night, had momentarily disturbed him. It had been close but muffled, unusual, for it was not the call of challenge, and for a moment he had thought that he knew the voice; but as it had not been repeated he was confident that the woodland was his and only his. For long minutes, early in the night, he had called and listened, called and listened, and the only reply he had heard was that of Kewick.

Across the clearing was the hardly discernible sound of another owl's wings, and the flurry of surprise close to a sprawling bramble. Kewick had checked her dive in an upward sweep, and her undercarriage had momentarily caught the dead skeleton of a long stretching thorn; a single feather trembled where only moments before a woodmouse had scuttled. Both owls had fed well. The mouse population was enormous

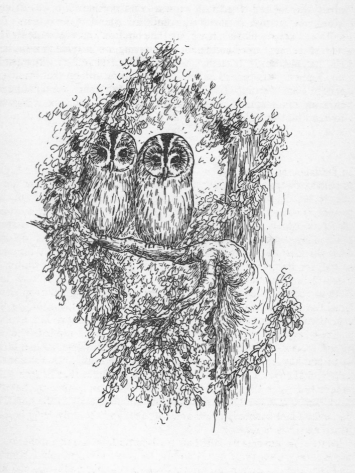

again; as always, it was reaching its peak in the dying year.

Ule called and flew again, up to the high tree at the top of the slope overlooking Longland. From there he could hear St Stephen's Falls, see across the flat-bottomed valley towards the northern arm of Dildawn's woodland, almost pick out the huddled shape of Greyfield Lodge behind the thin, massed shadows of the larches, and above the shadows the bright pinpricks and the round, glowing moon. That was his world and he called to it. Distant, down on Alder Island, Kewick heard him and replied. For long, silent minutes Ule stood still on that branch and watched and waited. Then there was a soft scratching against the high tree, an imperceptible shaking of a twig, for Ule had spread his wings, covered his day face, opened wide his brown eyes, and glided out into a sky full with rings of bright sound.

❧❦ EPILOGUE ❧❦

Ule died in early autumn, shot by mistake, a few years after his first year as a mature owl in Dildawn, but his son lives on to hunt in the acres which once resounded only to the cries of his father.

Damply the silence
Of oak and of hawthorn
Darkness brings with it
The crack of his doom.

Boundless above him
The stars are unwinking
Silent he comes on
The wings of his night.

Quietly gliding
Bringer of thunder
The hammer and axe
The blood and the wound.

High in the darkness
He perches and watches
Covers his day face
Blinks open his eyes.

Then in the blackness
He follows his senses
Rings of bright sound
In the valley which moves.

Clearly I hear them
The hunter and hunted
The shudder of wings
And the cries of the night.